BUILD A SOLAR TRACKER

How to Build a Dual Axis Sun Tracking System

by Michael T. Mruzek

BUILD A SOLAR TRACKER
Copyright © 2016 by Michael T. Mruzek

ISBN 978-0-9971958-0-4

Published by MTM Scientific, Inc.
P.O. Box 522 Clinton, Michigan 49236

Printed in USA by 48HrBooks of Akron, Ohio
First Edition

Dedication

This book is dedicated to two of my favorite childhood authors: G. Harry Stine for his book "Handbook of Model Rocketry", and D.S. Halacy, Jr. for his book "Fun with the Sun". Both of these authors' works encouraged me to explore technical pastimes as a youth, which eventually lead to a very rewarding career in engineering, and my continued interest in many other technical pursuits.

Table of Contents

About the Author 5

Preface 6

Introduction 7

Chapter 1: Solar Tracker Basics 9

Chapter 2: Mechanical Design 17

Chapter 3: Electrical Design 35

Chapter 4: Sensors 65

Chapter 5: Picaxe Microcontroller 85

Chapter 6: Software Control 107

Chapter 7: Tracker Operation 125

Chapter 8: Payloads 141

Chapter 9: New Directions 149

Chapter 10: Special Information 155

Chapter 11: Project Quick Start 161

Appendix: Source Code Listing 165

Index 191

About the Author

Born in Michigan in 1957, Mr. Mruzek was raised in the Southeastern corner of the "Great Lake State", near Lake Erie. He received his Bachelor of Science degree in Mechanical Engineering from the University of Michigan in 1979. He has subsequently worked at the Fermi National Accelerator Laboratory in Batavia, Illinois, at KMS Fusion, Inc., in Ann Arbor, Michigan, at General Electric in Milwaukee, Wisconsin and most recently at Stryker Instruments in Kalamazoo, Michigan.

In 2003, he founded MTM Scientific, Inc., which is a scientific resource company for technically inclined hobbyists and experimenters. He is also an amateur radio operator with call sign KC8SOA. He is the author of numerous technical papers covering such diverse topics as superconducting magnets, cryogenics, inertial confinement fusion and amateur radio astronomy. He is also inventor or co-inventor on five United States Patents.

Preface

Building solar trackers has been part of our life for approximately the last fifteen years. What began as a hobby has eventually become a small business: MTM Scientific, Inc. Our business specialty has included helping technically inclined individuals build and operate their own solar trackers. In that time we have accumulated a wealth of experience and "hands-on" knowledge of the craft with the assistance of our capable and creative customers. We hope to share that knowledge and experience in this book.

Our goal is to describe a dual axis solar tracker design with sufficient detail that the reader has the tools and understanding to modify the design for their own purposes. We can't wait to see where it goes from here!

Introduction

Building a dual axis solar tracker is a fairly advanced project which involves many different technical disciplines. The solar tracker project described here combines knowledge of astronomy, electronics, computers, software, optics and mechanics. In one sense, these related technical disciplines come together in a beautiful way that can help foster a broad-based understanding of the engineering world. Our hope is that this project will help you explore these interesting fields, and possibly add some points of interest to your knowledge in the areas you already master.

We expect you are anxious to get started on this project, and you may be tempted to thumb through this book and start building! We've anticipated that possibility, and therefore have included directions for making a "quick start" in Chapter 11. We have attempted to minimize repetition of material in the text, while at the same time anticipating that our readers may be jumping from topic to topic in non-sequential order.

Chapter 1: Solar Tracker Basics

In this chapter, we will discuss single and dual axis tracking, with an emphasis on various strategies for finding the Sun in the sky. We will explain how our dual axis tracker finds the Sun by using a sensor, and then storing certain information to make the next search faster. At the end of this chapter we list the specifications for the dual axis tracker we are building, with some photographs, to provide a project overview.

Daily and Seasonal Sun Motion

The Sun appears to move in the sky, tracing out a daily path from East to West. The Sun starts at the horizon at dawn, reaches a high point at solar noon in the middle of the day, and returns to the horizon at sunset. In addition to the daily motion, there is also a seasonal variation. In the Northern Hemisphere, the Sun is higher in the sky in Summer and lower in Winter. But despite these variations, the Sun's apparent path from one day to the next day is pretty nearly identical: We know the Sun will rise in the East, reach the highest point in the sky towards the South at solar noon, and set in the West. This typical day is shown graphically in Figure 1-1.

Suppose we used a watch and clipboard to record the position of the Sun. On the first day, we watch and wait for the Sun to rise to its highest point in the sky to the South and record the time. The next day we do the same thing. Would the recorded times be the same? No. The times would be different, but not by very much... perhaps by 30 seconds. Astronomers tell us the time difference depends on the time of year and location of the observer, and the exact time difference is precisely described by a formula known as the "equation of time".

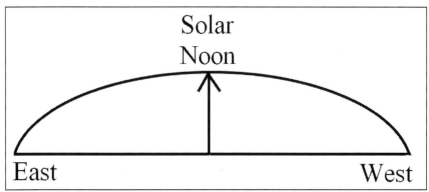

Figure 1-1. Path of the Sun in the sky on a typical day.

Therefore, from an engineering perspective, and to a pretty good approximation, the Sun's position in the sky today follows the same path it took yesterday, and the same path that it will follow tomorrow. So, if we find the Sun in the sky today and record the position, we can return to that same sky position tomorrow (at the same time) and be very close to the actual position. This presents an opportunity for smart sky searching that we will be using to advantage in this solar tracker design.

<u>Single and Dual Axis Tracking</u>

A solar tracker is designed to carry a payload, but not all payloads require the same Sun tracking accuracy. For example, a solar electric panel only requires approximate Sun aiming to generate full power output. However, another payload example is a parabolic collector. A parabolic collector must be aimed within a few degrees of the Sun's sky location, or the device simply won't work.

Dual axis solar tracking is most useful for payloads which benefit from direct and precise Sun aiming. That's because the additional cost and complexity of a solar tracker is not insignificant, and that's especially true for a dual axis design. Sometimes, the simpler and more economical solution for a solar application is simply adding more stationary collectors.

Some payloads are absolutely ideal for dual axis solar tracking applications. These payloads typically use optical methods to concentrate sunlight, such as parabolic dishes and lenses. With these applications, consideration must be given to the tradeoff between automated dual axis tracking versus manual or single axis tracking. However, these applications tend to have a unique aspect to them, due to the spectacular results of concentrating sunlight, especially in large amounts and at high temperatures.

Calculate and Aim Method

We do not use the "calculate and aim" method of solar tracking for this project, but we will briefly describe the approach and explain why it's not used here.

Considered from a purely theoretical point of view, the apparent position of the Sun in the sky depends upon the observer's location, time and date. The Sun's position can then be accurately determined by a mathematical formula which uses the location, time, and date information to perform an aiming calculation. The basic idea with this approach is to create a tracker controller with the ability to calculate the Sun's position, and then precisely aim the solar tracker at that calculated position in the sky. This is much more difficult to accomplish than you might think!

For this approach to work you must have the following information: 1) The latitude and longitude of the location, 2) The correct time, 3) The correct date, and 4) Real-time feedback of the actual aiming coordinates from the solar tracker. Additionally, the accuracy of each of these pieces of information, including the accuracy of the equation and the calculating engine, all directly impact the final quality of the "blind" aim.

The usual approach with this method is to use a computing microcontroller with a battery-driven real time clock (RTC) module. The operator provides the latitude, longitude, time and date to the software in the microcontroller via a user interface. Additionally, the microcontroller

11

has data acquisition capability, such that sensors on the tracker can report the real-time aiming information back to the controller.

This approach has several practical difficulties: 1) User input at startup is required to provide the position, time and date, 2) Battery backup and maintenance is required for the real time clock, 3) The real-time clock must maintain accuracy over long time spans, potentially measured in years, and 4) Sensors on the tracker must have the ability and absolute accuracy to report the spatial aim in three dimensional space.

Faced with these technical challenges, the usual course of action (to address these issues) is to include additional technology in the design. For example, a Global Positioning System (GPS) module can be included as part of the control system. Another possibility is to network the tracker controller using 3G, 4G or WiFi communication. However, the pitfall with including additional technology is the introduction of additional dependencies on other complex systems. For example, GPS depends not only on the existence of multiple satellites in the sky; it also depends on the long term stability of the signal protocol being used for the GPS beacon signal. (Imagine a vintage solar tracker that comically attempts to use a dialup modem to connect with "America Online" to get the time and date.)

Our design goal is a solar tracking controller with absolutely no dependencies on external systems. Stated a different way: Our goal is a solar tracker controller which can be stored away for decades and put back into service, at any location, at a moment's notice, and with no need of external inputs from the user or other technical systems. We want a solar tracker that simply finds the Sun. Additionally, we might hope for a tracker which can "learn" over the course of time, and find the Sun faster and faster as the days go by.

Sky Search Method

Another broad category of solar tracker is the type which searches for the Sun's position in the sky using a sensor or sensor array. Sunlight is easily detected with a variety of different sensors, such as photocells, photodiodes, solar cells and light emitting diodes (LED). However, simply detecting whether sunlight is present is not enough information. Aiming at the Sun also requires information about the sunlight's direction. For that reason an array of sensors is often used, with a controller or logic circuit decoding the individual sensor readings to determine the sunlight's true direction.

Figure 1-2. The completed dual axis solar tracker.

Searching for the Sun in the sky using a sensor has several advantages. With a sensor, the controller has real time feedback about the quality of the aim. That feedback can therefore be used to improve the aim. And although the Sun must be present for the sensor method to work, it really isn't much of an issue since we don't usually need to aim the tracker if the Sun isn't shining.

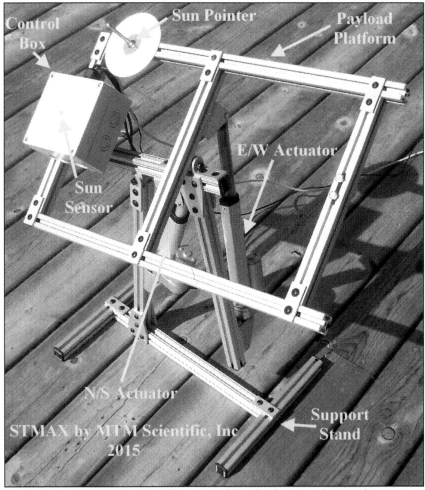

Figure 1-3. Key elements of the dual axis solar tracker.

The only real disadvantage of this approach is the requirement to find the Sun using a sky search, which may require more movement and articulation of the solar tracker compared to a definite aiming direction provided by a calculation. However, that disadvantage only exists to the extent that we aren't able to quickly and efficiently find the Sun based on the sensor system signal. As we shall see, with the right choice of sensor and software logic, finding the Sun in the sky is actually pretty easy to do. In fact, we can almost get to the point of moving directly to the correct sky location by devising an optimized searching strategy.

Therefore, our solar tracker project uses a sensor to find the Sun. But our solar tracker also has a clever twist: Remembering where the Sun was found. In this project, the tracker controller maintains an internal clock based on solar time, and records the position of the Sun after it is found. The Sun position data is logged into a database, and the data is later used to find the Sun more quickly and efficiently, on the following days. In some ways, our solar tracker incorporates the best features of both Sun tracking methods.

However, for this method to work well, we need to incorporate a very specific style of solar tracker mounting structure. We call this mechanical style the "tilt-tilt" tracker approach. We will say more about this in the next chapter when we discuss the mechanical design in detail.

Specifications: Dual Axis Solar Tracker

This book focuses on building a dual axis solar tracker with specific design guidelines and directions. We realize that many people will make changes and modify the design for their own purposes. In fact we fully expect that! But, we have to start somewhere. We start with a solar tracker called our "baseline design". The key components in the baseline design are shown and labeled in Figure 1-3, and the technical specifications are listed in Figure 1-4.

SPECIFICATIONS: DUAL AXIS SOLAR TRACKER

Sun Tracking Motion	Dual Axis (North/South and East/West)
Prime Movers	Linear Actuators, 4 inch (10 cm) and 6 inch (15 cm) Travel
Sun Sensor	Light Emitting Diode (LED)
Power Supply	12 VDC / 2 Amps
Control	Microprocessor (Picaxe-20X2)
Operating Mode	Automatic and Fully Independent
Data and Status Reporting	RS-232 Serial Output Available
Tracking Updates	Every 6 minutes (Optional 30 minutes)
Tracking Accuracy	+/- 10 degrees
Maximum Payload Weight	Approximately 20 pounds (9.1 Kg)
Payload Platform Size	12 inches X 24 inches (30 cm X 61 cm)
Structural Frame	80/20 Aluminum Framing System
Range of Motion	North/South = 90 Degrees, East/West = 150 Degrees

Figure 1-4. Specifications of the "baseline" dual axis solar tracker.

Chapter Two: Mechanical Design

Building a dual axis solar tracker requires a mechanical structure which can aim at different sky positions to follow the Sun, wherever it may be. Roughly speaking, the tracker structure should be capable of pointing to the Eastern horizon at sunrise, following the Sun during the day, and pointing to the Western horizon at sunset. There are various solutions to this mechanical design challenge. However, one particular mechanical solution has important design advantages in relation to other parts of our solar tracker project, which we will now describe.

Tilt-Tilt Solar Trackers

We call our preferred mechanical design solution for the tracker hardware the "tilt-tilt" solar tracker. A simple mechanical example of the tilt-tilt style of solar tracker is shown in Figure 2-2. In this mechanical design approach the hardware makes two independent tilting motions to follow the Sun: A North-South tilt and an East-West tilt.

The choice of a tilt-tilt mechanical structure for doing sky aiming may seem completely arbitrary. For example, another type of mechanical design would be a "tilt-rotate" solar tracker. In a tilt-rotate tracker the aiming motion for following the Sun from East to West is performed by a rotation around the vertical axis. The different tracking motions are shown in Figure 2-1.

The important difference between the tilt-tilt and tilt-rotate style of design is due to a consideration which has nothing to do with mechanics, but rather with the sensor module we will be using to measure the solar tracker's aiming direction.

Imagine that we place a pair of angle meters on the tilt-tilt solar tracker platform. The angle meters measure the angle of the platform with respect to the vertical, as determined by gravity. Whenever the

17

platform moves, either East-West or North-South, an angle meter will detect a change. However, with the same angle meters on the tilt-rotate tracker only the North-South motion is detectable. The East-West rotational motion cannot be detected by angle meters which use gravity as a reference. *Here's the bottom line: If we design the mechanical structure to move with a tilt-tilt motion we can use a special low-cost angle sensor to monitor the tracker's aim simply and accurately.*

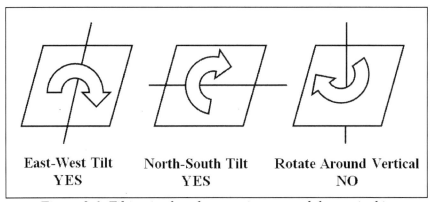

East-West Tilt	North-South Tilt	Rotate Around Vertical
YES	**YES**	**NO**

Figure 2-1. Tilting is okay, but rotating around the vertical is not.

Additionally, constructing a solar tracker with movement of the tilt-tilt style really is no more difficult than any other style, and actually is quite suitable with the use of linear actuators for moving things. The basic design uses a base beam which is arranged to move to and fro on a North-South axis. On this base beam is attached the payload platform. The payload platform is hinged to the base beam and moves to and fro on an East-West axis. This simple mechanical arrangement provides very good sky aiming coverage and is also easy to build.

A tilt-tilt platform can be built using various materials and design elements. Our first tilt-tilt platform, shown in Figure 2-2, was built using ordinary lumber from a home improvement center. The North-South base beam was made with 2" x 4" boards, and the axle pivot point is simply a rather long ¼" bolt. The payload platform is also made of dimensional lumber, and uses a simple lag screw for the hinged pivot point. There is nothing special or particular about this style of construction, and you can easily use or adapt any other materials you may already have available. You will notice here that we have used linear actuators with long travel extensions, since this prototype tracker was larger than our baseline design.

Figure 2-2. Example of tilt-tilt platform built using wood.

Figure 2-3. A tilt-tilt frame built using 80/20 structural framing.

In our preferred approach to building a tilt-tilt platform we use a modular structural framing system called "80/20". For all intents and purposes, 80/20 is an "erector set" for engineers. The basic framing members are made of extruded aluminum with a one inch square cross section. A complete assortment of mechanical framing connectors are also available from 80/20, which includes rugged hinges for dynamic movement. Additionally, each of the 80/20 components have a specific name and unique part number. Part numbers are useful for purchasing the components from suppliers. Part numbers are also helpful for sourcing the components from online marketplaces, such as Ebay or Amazon. Since the 80/20 components are connected using adjustable fasteners, it is also a simple matter to make adjustments to the structure during your design phase. As a bonus, the 80/20 parts can be reused in other projects, if your interests or design intent changes during the course of your build and field trials.

| | Notes: | Bill of Materials creates 1 kits. |
| | | STMAX - Base Kit |

TAG	Part#	Qty	Length Each (or area)	Units	Total Wgt (lbs)	Description Note:all extrusion dimensions start at the left end
A	1010	2	24.000	IN	2.11	1" X 1" T-SLOTTED EXTRUSION
B	1010	4	15.000	IN	2.64	1" X 1" T-SLOTTED EXTRUSION
C	1010	5	12.000	IN	2.64	1" X 1" T-SLOTTED EXTRUSION
	7005	11		EA		Cut to Length 1" x 1" T-Slot and Tube
D	2015	11		EA	0.07	1010 END CAP BLACK W/PUSH-INS
E	4107	6		EA	0.18	10 S 2 HOLE JOINING STRIP
F	4141	6		EA	0.51	10 S 4 HOLE TEE JOINING PLATE
G	4172	4		EA	0.32	COUNTERSINK "L" PIVOT ARM (REPLACES DISCONTINUED 4193)
H	4181	3		EA	0.29	10 S 0 DEGREE LIVING NUB
I	4185	2		EA	0.18	ARM FOR 1010 LIVING HINGE
	3275	2		EA	0.02	10 S ECON T-NUT 8-32 THREAD
	3393	50		EA	0.90	1/4-20 X 1/2" BHSCS, ECON T-NUT
	3501	3		EA	0.12	10 S LIVING HINGE KIT

Figure 2-4. Parts list for the 80/20 tilt-tilt frame.

An example of a tilt-tilt platform built using 80/20 is shown in Figure 2-3. The parts list for this particular tracker design is provided in Figure 2-4. This tilt-tilt platform can easily be built in a few hours, once you acquire all the parts.

Assembly of the platform is done with button head socket cap screws and a ball end Allen driver of 5/32" dimension. The frame described here has been built using the 1010 extrusion, which has a nominal 1" square cross-section. Heavier duty extrusions are also available if you decide to build a larger tracker in the future.

An isometric view of the 80/20 frame construction is shown in Figure 2-5. The actual placement of the structural elements is not especially critical, and the design is symmetric in most respects. A side view of the 80/20 frame is shown in Figure 2-6, with some overall dimensions provided to assist with assembly.

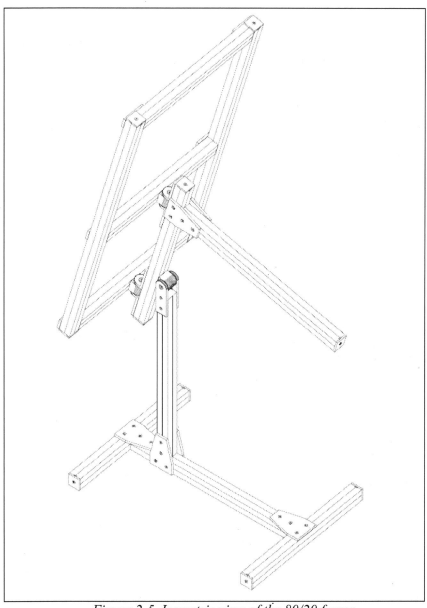

Figure 2-5. Isometric view of the 80/20 frame.

The 80/20 frame is designed to be assembled using standard connectors compatible with the structural elements. The most standard connector is a button head flange screw used with a stamped flat nut, called an "economy nut", as shown in Figure 2-9. These fasteners are easily assembled using a ball end Allen driver, as shown in Figure 2-7.

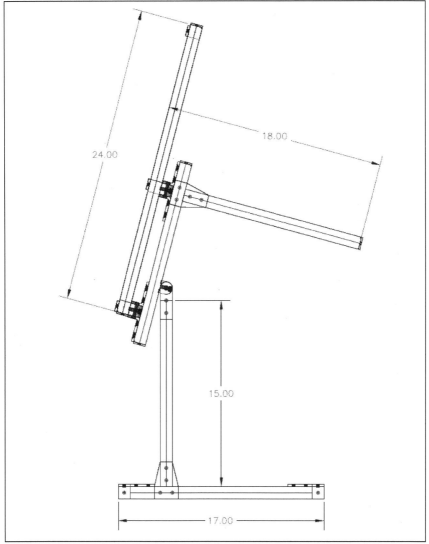

Figure 2-6. A side view of the 80/20 tilt-tilt platform frame.

The flanges used for connecting the structural frame together are also a standardized design, and are generally referred to with descriptive names that reference the number of holes in them.

The dynamic parts of the structural elements are called "hinges". This solar tracker design uses two different hinge types. Both types are referred to as "living hinges", and they are shown in greater detail in Figure 2-8. The hinges should be carefully assembled according to the instructions included with them by 80/20. This assures proper operation. The hinge hardware is designed with optimal mechanical clearances, such that the fasteners can by "tightened down" without binding the action of the hinge. Correct assembly of the hinge hardware is very important.

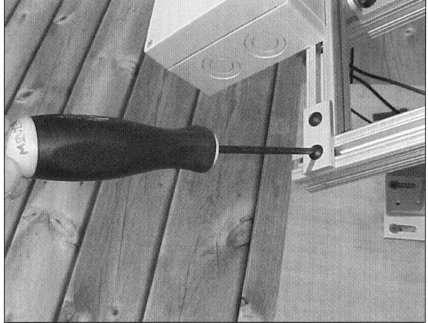

Figure 2-7. Assembly and ddisassembly using a 5/32" ball driver.

The payload platform in our baseline design is 12 inches wide by 24 inches long. There is nothing especially critical about these dimensions, and for a long time our prototype payload platform was simply 12 inches square. Note that the enclosure box for mounting the controller is attached to the movable portion of the payload platform. This is necessary because the angle sensor module is inside the enclosure. The angle sensor must be on the moving tilt-tilt frame to measure the aiming direction of the solar tracker.

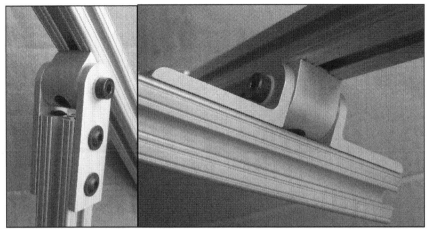

Figure 2-8 North-South and East-West living hinges from 80/20.

Figure 2-9. Button head socket cap screw with economy nut.

A detailed photo of the solar tracker's base assembly is shown in Figure 2-10, to assist with assembly of the frame. There also isn't anything especially critical regarding the base assembly, and you may prefer to modify the details of the mounting arrangement for your own specific purposes.

Figure 2-10. Details of the 80/20 base frame.

More construction details of the payload platform are shown in Figure 2-11.

Figure 2-11. Details of a typical corner on the payload platform.

An end view of the 1010 extrusion profile is shown in Figure 2-12. The slots in the extrusion are made to hold the economy nuts. The economy nuts slide into the slots for easy positioning, but are prevented from rotating for the actual "tightening-down". This is a great convenience for adjusting the structure's range of motion. The adjustments can be made quickly and easily using simple hand tools on the fly.

If at some point in the project you decide a more permanent mounting method is desirable, we'd like to mention that 80/20 offers an accessory for that purpose, as shown in Figure 2-13. This part is called the "Floor Mount Base", and is identified as Part #2380 by 80/20. In practice, we have mounted this base to a wooden platform by simply using ordinary wood screws.

Figure 2-12. End view of the "1010" extrusion from 80/20.

Sun Pointer

The quality of aim of your solar tracker with respect to the location of the Sun in the sky can be difficult to judge when you are doing field work. Fortunately, the quality of aim can be rapidly and precisely determined with the aid of a simple tool. You will find it helpful to include a Sun pointer on your solar tracker, as shown in Figure 2-14. The Sun pointer consists of a threaded bolt stud, 3 inches long that has been attached to the frame using an economy nut, fender washer and flanged nut. The circular shadow plate is nothing more than a CD-ROM disk with a white top face.

Figure 2-13. Alternative method for mounting upright support.

Enclosure

The solar tracker controller is a printed circuit board (PCB) with electronic components. For initial testing it is okay to use the board outside the enclosure, and in fact we did that for much of our early testing. Eventually though, you will want to mount the controller inside a weather tight enclosure. The enclosure we prefer to use is shown in Figure 2-15.

The printed circuit board available for this project was designed for mounting inside a specific weather-tight enclosure, with nominal size of 5 x 5 x 3 inches. The PCB has two mounting holes which align with mounting screw locations inside the enclosure. The enclosure is available from McMaster-Carr (#7360K63, color gray). The mounting holes on the PCB are clearly marked with labels.

One of the nice features of the enclosure are the prescored knockouts for mounting a cable feedthrough. The knockouts can be removed with a sharp rap from a large flat bladed screwdriver. Also, the box easily mounts to the 80/20 frame using a pair of #8-32 screws, when combined with a pair of the special economy nuts listed in the parts list.

When mounting the PCB inside the enclosure, make sure the arrow pointing South is aligned correctly with regards to the tilt-tilt frame.

A few minor modifications of the box are necessary for it to be used in this project. The first modification is for mounting the enclosure to the 80/20 frame. The box is mounted using two #8-32 screws. We have found it is helpful for the mounting to remove the cover and drill out the holes slightly using a 13/64" drill, as shown. The other modification is to drill a hole for the LED sensor in the top lid. This hole is also 13/64" diameter, so the same drill bit can be used. The sensor and mounting method are described in greater detail in Chapter 4.

Figure 2-14. Short threaded rod and CD disk used as a Sun pointer.

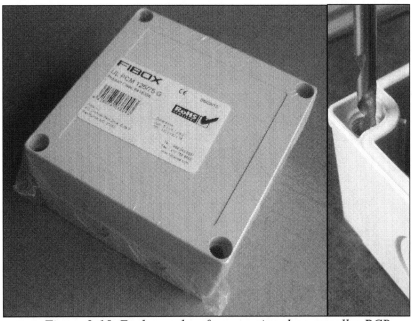

Figure 2-15. Enclosure box for mounting the controller PCB.

Mechanical Parts List

The complete list of additional mechanical items required to complete this solar tracker project are listed in Figure 2-16. We have listed part number information for purchasing these items directly from commercial suppliers. It's also possible to find these parts elsewhere, for example by searching on Ebay, Google or Amazon.

We have provided a detailed parts list for building the solar tracker. However, we also appreciate that many people will have a limited budget for doing this project. The best way to keep costs low is to carefully examine the part description, consider the purpose of the part, and then review listings on websites (such as Ebay) to find the best price. It is often possible to obtain items online at very attractive prices, especially if you plan ahead and purchase the items before they are actually needed. In that way, a shipping delay of a few weeks (or more) is not an issue.

Barebones Mechanical Setup

We know that many experimenters are on a budget, and keeping initial development costs low is a high priority. At the same time, you may still have the ultimate goal of building a complete tracker exactly according to these plans. We'd like to suggest the possibility of starting with a "barebones" tilt-tilt platform mechanical setup.

A barebones tilt-tilt platform focuses on acquiring the correct dynamically hinged parts, combined with just enough of the structural frame, such that you can proceed with field testing. Basically, all you really need to get started are four pieces of extrusion, two flanges and two hinge assemblies. A photo of such a barebones setup is shown in Figure 2-17. The parts list for a barebones setup is provided in Figure 2-18. All the parts for building a barebones setup are available on Ebay.

Solar Tracker Parts List: Mechanical & Miscellaneous

Component Name	Qty	Manufacturer / Part Number / Details	Supplier	Supplier Part Number / Notes
Linear Actuator*, 4 inch travel	1	Pololu / LACT4-12V-20	pololu.com	20:1 Gearbox, 110 lbf, 0.5 in/sec
Linear Actuator*, 6 inch travel	1	Pololu / LACT6-12V-20	pololu.com	20:1 Gearbox, 110 lbf, 0.5 in/sec
Clevis Bracket* (Linear Actuator)	4	Includes clevis and cotter pins required	progressiveautomations.com	#BRK-14
Washers* (Used for Brackets)	8	¼ inch ID, Zinc Plated Steel	mcmaster.com	#98023A029
Enclosure Box (130x130x75 mm)	1	Fibox, Inc. / Product Code 6416308	mcmaster.com	#7360K63
Feed Through (4 Hole, Modified)	1	Drill out holes as needed	mcmaster.com	#7807K39
Enclosure Box Mounting Screws*	2	#8-32 X 5/8 inches (9/64 in Allen Key)	mcmaster.com	#92196A196
Silicone Sealant*	As Required	General Electric, Black	mcmaster.com	#7545A461
Wire Cable* (Sun Sensor Leads)	6 inches	24 Gauge, 2 Conductor, Red/Black	mcmaster.com	#969T1
Shrink tube* (Sun Sensor Leads)	3 inches	Polyolefin, Black	mcmaster.com	#7856K11
CD-R Disk* (Sun Pointer)	1	Verbatim / VER96189 / White Printable	officedepot.com	#879655
Threaded Rod* (Sun Pointer)	1	¼-20 Thread, 3 inches long	mcmaster.com	#95475A554
Fender Washer* (Sun Pointer)	1	¼ inch ID, 1.50 inch OD	mcmaster.com	#91090A113
Flange Nut* (Sun Pointer)	1	¼-20 Thread, Zinc Plated	mcmaster.com	#99904A101
Economy Nut (Sun Pointer)	1	Note: Included in 80/20 List	8020.net	Note: Included in 80/20 List
Compass* (Optional)	1	Plastic Compass for tracker setup	mcmaster.com	#20185A18
Serial Cable (10 foot, Modified)	1	DB-9 Serial Cable (Cut off male end)	mcmaster.com	#7925K22
Assembly Tool* (Allen Ball Driver)	1	5/32 inch Hex, Ball-End	mcmaster.com	#5497A29
Drill Bit* (Box Modification)	1	13/64 inch (Drill hole for LED, Screws)	mcmaster.com	#2901A121

*The items with an asterisk can often be sourced from your junk box, hardware store, or EBAY for substantial cost savings.

Figure 2-16. Mechanical parts required to build the tracker.

The barebones parts are used to create an upright beam, North-South pivot and East-West pivot. With this approach, you can start with a minimum of purchased 80/20 items, and add the other 80/20 parts as you proceed with the project. Nothing is wasted. Of course, you must also improvise a base for mounting the setup. But that can be something as simple as a piece of wood or even a large vise or clamp.

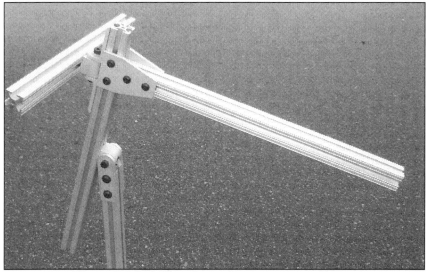

Figure 2-17. A "barebones" setup to start the project.

Parts List for "Barebones" Tracker Setup			
Quantity	80/20 Number	Item Description	Purpose
2	1010 Extrusion	12.0 inches long	N/S Beam and E/W Beam
2	1010 Extrusion	15.0 inches long	Vertical Upright and Actuator Beam
2	4141	4 Hole Tee Joining Plate	Connect Actuator Beam to N/S Beam
2	4172	"L" Pivot Arm	Hinge for E/W Beam
2	4181	Zero Degree Living Nub	Nub for Hinges
2	4185	Arm for Living Hinge	Hinge for N/S Beam
2	3275	Economy T-Nut 8-32 Thread	Mount for Enclosure
20	3393	Economy Bolt & T-Nut 1/-20 Thread	Fasteners
2	3501	Living Hinge Kit	Hardware for Hinges
Note: These parts are often available on EBAY. This list is a subset of the full tracker project.			

Figure 2-18. Parts list to build a "barebones" tracker frame.

Chapter Three: Electrical Design

Having decided upon a tilt-tilt style mechanical arrangement, as described in Chapter 2, we now need an electrical setup to move the North-South and East-West linear actuators. Our first order of business in this chapter will be to describe the electro-mechanical aspects of the tracker project, such as the linear actuators, relays and power supplies.

Next, we will examine details of the electrical circuit and electronic components. We begin our discussion of the electronics with a description of several sub-circuits. Each sub-circuit performs a specific function. Then, we'll move on to discussing the electrical circuit in its entirety.

Finally, we discuss the printed circuit board design and assembly. The quickest and least expensive path for building this project is to use the circuit board that's available. However, using the circuit board is not a requirement, especially if you have an interest in designing your own PCB.

The complete electronic parts list and electronic circuit schematic are presented at the end of this chapter.

Linear Actuators

A linear actuator is a device which uses electrical power in the form of direct current (DC) electricity to operate a motor, which in turn is designed to create a powerful linear motion using an internal powerscrew mechanism. A linear actuator is rated by the amount of linear travel motion (in inches), and also the force it can create when moving (in pounds). For example, in our project we have chosen a 6" linear actuator for the East-West motion, and a 4" linear actuator for the North-South motion. Both actuators are capable of exerting 225 pounds force.

What happens when a linear actuator reaches the end of travel, after either extending or retracting fully? Well, the answer to that is actually quite simple: it stops. Inside a linear actuator there are limit switches to stop the motion at the limits of travel. When a limit switch is tripped, the linear actuator is only allowed to resume motion again by going in the opposite direction. This is accomplished internally with a diode connected in parallel across the terminals of each limit switch.

Linear actuators operate in a manner which is actually quite ideal for our solar tracker application. We can confidently energize the linear actuators to move in either direction, without worry that the mechanism might be going "too far". The linear actuators are self-protected by their internal limit switches.

This project uses two different 12VDC linear actuators. For the North-South motion we use a linear actuator with four inches of travel, and for the East-West motion we use a linear actuator with six inches of travel. When purchasing linear actuators for your project, one important consideration is to select linear actuators which are rated for slow speeds and high forces. The linear actuators shown in Figure 3-1 are rated for a speed of about ¼ inch per second, and a maximum force of 225 pounds. Generally, you will find that the slowest moving actuators also provide the highest force, which is an ideal combination for our solar tracker.

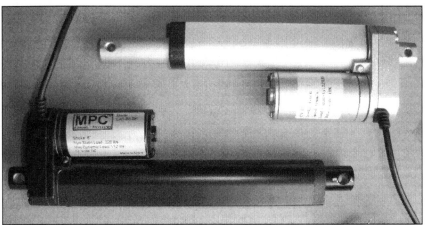

Figure 3-1. Linear Actuators with 4 and 6 inch travel.

The linear actuators are attached to the moving structural frame of the solar tracker using clevis pin brackets, as shown in Figure 3-2 and Figure 3-3. These brackets simplify the mechanical construction, and also have the benefit of being adjustable in regards to position. These brackets are often available from the supplier of the linear actuators, and they also can be widely found on Ebay.

The electrical connections for actuators are simple. There are only two wires. Usually the wires are color-coded red and black, to indicate positive and negative polarity. The wires are attached directly to the controller using simple screw terminals on the PCB. If during testing a linear actuator is moving in the wrong direction (i.e. West instead of East) simply swap the positive and negative leads at the screw terminal connector.

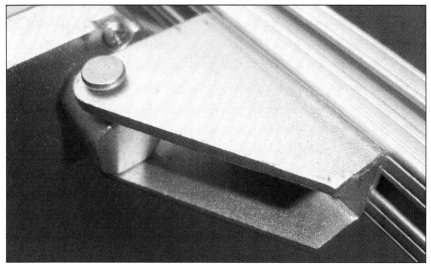

Figure 3-2. Clevis brackets secure the linear actuator to the frame.

Project Power Supply

This solar tracker project uses 12VDC as the main electrical power source. The 12VDC can be supplied by a standard power supply or a battery. We suggest using a standard power supply during the testing phase. Power supplies suitable for this project are inexpensive, reliable and readily available. We have found that a 12VDC supply with a 2 amp output rating works great in this application. Some examples of suitable power supplies are shown in Figure 3-4. The type of 12VDC power supply that plugs directly into a 120VAC household power outlet is ideal.

The linear actuators operate directly from the 12VDC power. The same 12VDC power also feeds a circuit for creating 5VDC power. The 5VDC power is used for operating various controller electronics, such as the microcontroller and digital electronics.

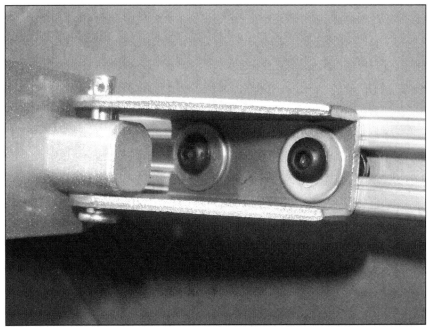

Figure 3-3. The bracket attaches easily to the 80/20 extrusion.

The 12VDC power supply circuit is shown in Figure 3-4. The circuit design includes several important safety features. The first precaution is a fuse. Generally, good operating practice is to use the smallest amperage fuse which works reliably in the application. In that regard, we have found a 2 amp fuse works well for this project. The largest possible fuse size is 8 amps. (The relays used in the controller have a maximum current rating of 8 amps.) When selecting a fuse type we suggest using a "slow-blow" fuse, which you will find has been specified in the parts list.

The 12VDC power supply circuit also has input polarity protection as a safety feature. Whenever DC power is applied to a circuit, it is always possible for the polarity to be accidently applied in reverse. A polarity protection diode is included in the 12VDC power supply circuit. That's the purpose of the 10A10 diode. So, if you accidentally reverse the positive and negative leads of the input power supply, circuit damage will be avoided. In that case, the controller won't "power-up" and it should be a simple matter to find the mistake.

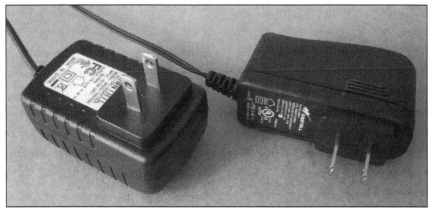

Figure 3-4. Examples of simple 12VDC power supplies.

Power Supply +5VDC

The solar tracker circuit design includes a 5VDC power supply. The 5VDC power supply is derived from the main 12VDC power supply. The circuit details of the power supply circuit are shown in Figure 3-5. The 5VDC supply provides power to the controller electronics, such as the microcontroller, watchdog timer circuit, and most of the sensors.

The 5VDC power supply circuit is designed to generate a precise and stable voltage reference source. Also, special emphasis has been placed on preventing noise spikes in the power supply. Noise spikes could potentially affect sensitive electrical components in the controller, such as the microcontroller and other digital devices.

The LM7805 is an integrated circuit (IC) voltage regulator which converts 12VDC input power to 5VDC output power. The LM7805 is a simple device with only three connections: voltage input, ground connection and stable 5VDC output. The output of the LM7805 voltage regulator is additionally stabilized with a large 470uF electrolytic capacitor.

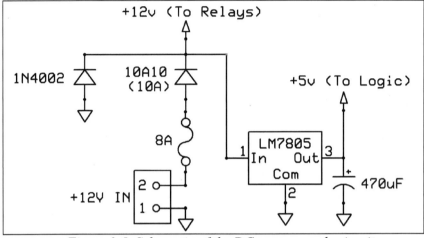

Figure 3-5. Schematic of the DC power supply circuits.

Watchdog Timer

This solar tracker controller includes a special circuit function known as a "watchdog timer". The purpose of a watchdog timer is to monitor operation of the microcontroller and trigger a restart if the controller stops working correctly. This function is much like rebooting your computer. When a computer or microcontroller is controlling unattended electrical hardware (such as a solar tracker) it is generally a good idea to include a watchdog timer. That's because it is always possible that the computer code will encounter a programming error, electrical noise or incorrect input conditions which prevent the software from continuing to execute. The watchdog timer is an automatic shutdown and reboot mechanism, which allows system recovery from abnormal situations.

The basic strategy for implementing a watchdog timer is to start with a counting clock. The clock is regulated by a timekeeper called the "oscillator". Every time the clock ticks, we count. When the count reaches a preset point, we send a command to shut down the computer.

The only way to prevent the shutdown is for the computer to send a signal to reset the counter and start over again. Fortunately, this entire process can be performed by a single IC, called a "ripple binary counter". The pinout of the ripple binary counter which we use (74HC4060) is shown in Figure 3-6.

A schematic of the watchdog timer circuit is shown in Figure 3-7. The active component in the circuit is a 74HC4060 integrated circuit. This IC is a combined oscillator and counter. The oscillator is a basic resistive and capacitive type, sometimes called an "R/C" clock. The counter is a binary ripple type, which means the count from each binary stage is automatically sent to the next stage. With 14 stages the counter can count to a maximum of 16,384 pulses. When the maximum count is reached the IC triggers an output signal to a BS250 field effect transistor (FET), which shuts down the microcontroller. The FET controls power to the Picaxe microcontroller, so if the shutdown count is reached, the controller is rebooted.

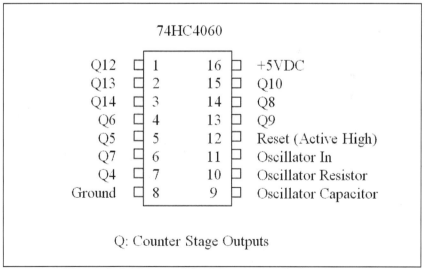

Figure 3-6. Pinout of the 14 stage ripple binary counter.

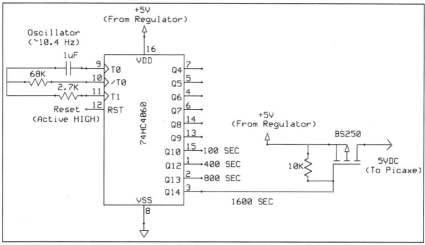

Figure 3-7. Circuit diagram of the watchdog timer.

Of course, we don't want the watchdog timer to be rebooting the microcontroller during normal operation. A reboot should only happen if there is a problem. The solution is to have the microcontroller periodically send a reset signal to the counter. The reset signal stops the counting and tells the watchdog timer to "start over again". That is the purpose of the reset signal from the microcontroller going to pin 12 on the 74HC4060 counter.

With the specific oscillator timing elements chosen for our circuit, the reset signal from the microcontroller must be received at least every 17 minutes. However, in practice, we've written the computer code to send the reset signal about every minute, since there is no harm in resetting the counter more frequently.

When the microcontroller is shut down it will remain "OFF" for 17 minutes. After that time the microcontroller will reboot and the solar tracker will restart operation, just as if it had been freshly plugged-in. In normal use you should never experience this reset process. However, if there is ever a problem, it's good to know the equipment will recover automatically.

Relay Operation → why not a transistor

The Picaxe microcontroller controls the operation
actuators. The linear actuators are heavy duty electromechan~~~~ ~~
and they can't be operated directly from the output of the microcontroller.
Instead, the output from the microcontroller is routed to small signal
transistors, which in turn actuate relays, which in turn operate the linear
actuators. The relays used for this solar tracker are a standard
electromechanical design, and were specifically chosen for their long
term reliability and duty rating. We have used this same relay for many
other solar tracker projects, and it has a solid track record.

The interior construction of a typical relay is shown in Figure 3-8. A
relay consists of a coil which becomes magnetic when power is applied.
The magnet coil attracts a piece of iron which is electrically connected
by a wire to a terminal, usually called "common", or "COM" for short.
When the relay is not energized the spring holds the common contact
against a terminal called "normally closed" or "NC" for short. When the
coil is energized the common terminal moves and makes electrical
contact with the other terminal called "normally open", or "NO" for
short. This switching arrangement is both simple and effective. Relays
are used in many different types of electrical power machinery.

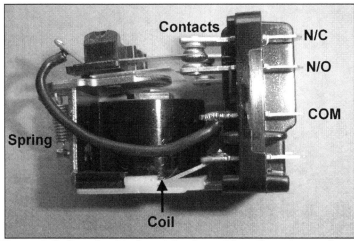

Figure 3-8. Standard industrial relay with coil, spring and contacts.

The relays used in our project are identical internally to the example we've described, but they have a plastic protective case to prevent damage to the parts, as shown in Figure 3-9. We have also chosen relays which have sockets available for them. The sockets make it very easy to replace the relays in the future, if maintenance or repair should ever be necessary.

Relay Circuit

The Picaxe microcontroller controls four relays using four output channel pins, as detailed in the schematic. The connection circuit for the two North-South relays is shown in Figure 3-11. (The East-West circuit is similar.) This special relay wiring configuration allows movement of the actuator in either direction by means of only two microcontroller signals. The two signals simply reverse the applied polarity of the DC power provided to the linear actuator.

Figure 3-9. Relays and sockets used in the solar tracker controller.

The Picaxe output channels are not directly connected to the relay coils. The Picaxe output channels are first buffered using small signal transistors. The transistors buffer and amplify the electrical signal for actuation of the relay coils. The transistors are a general purpose 2N3904 type, technically called an NPN bipolar junction semiconductor. Notice that one transistor is used for each of the four relay coils. Each signal line from the Picaxe includes a 10K resistor as a buffer to protect the Picaxe output pin, since preventing damage to the microcontroller is a high priority.

Because the actuator coils in the relays are inductive, and because we are switching the coils with transistors, special care must be taken to handle the inductive "kickback" from the coils. That is the purpose of the diodes connected across the relay coil leads. The diodes are type 1N4002. These diodes are very important. Without the diodes, the "make and break" of the relay coils would induce voltage spikes and damage the switching transistors.

The relay circuit includes toggle switches for actuating the relays manually, as shown in Figure 3-10. This feature is especially useful during initial setup and testing of the solar tracker. The manual switches are a convenient method for verifying that the polarity of the linear actuator connections are correct. The switches are also convenient for adjusting the travel limits of the actuators. You can use the switches to extend and retract the actuators while checking their mechanical action. The manual switches will work without the microcontroller installed, so you can check this part of the setup early in your project. This is perfect for making adjustments and setting the limits of travel on the tilt-tilt frame, before proceeding to automatic control with the solar tracker controller.

Printed Circuit Board Design

A printed circuit board (PCB) is a flat fiberglass board with etched copper plating on both sides, designed for mounting electrical components and for making electrical connections between the components. A PCB makes it much easier to assemble a complex electrical circuit, since the process basically involves inserting the component leads into the PCB holes and soldering them in place.

Figure 3-10. A pair of toggle switches used for manual operation.

A printed circuit board is available for this project, and using the PCB will generally be the quickest, easiest and least expensive path to building this project. However, we will provide some additional information about printed circuit boards, since we suspect some project builders will have an interest in modifying the design, or creating their own PCB.

In the past, printed circuit boards were fairly difficult to design and construct because the design process was done manually on a drafting board using black tracing tape and a knife edge. And creating the artwork was only part of the challenge. Special equipment and chemicals were also required to etch the copper traces onto the board. Optionally, the boards could be fabricated by a commercial supply house, but that was generally an expensive proposition, especially in small hobby-sized quantities.

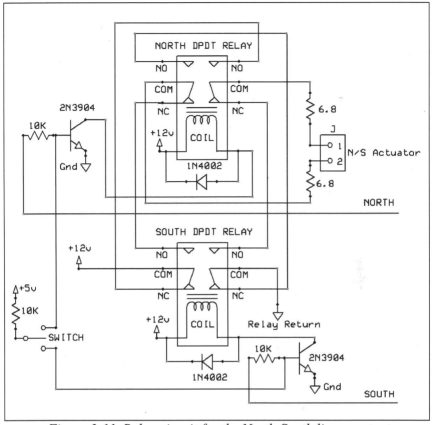

Figure 3-11. Relay circuit for the North-South linear actuator.

Designing and producing custom printed circuit boards for hobby projects has become much easier in the last few years with the advent of personal computers. Now it is relatively easy to use computer software to design a PCB. It's also a fairly simple matter to purchase small quantities of your design from a specialty PCB supplier. These specialty suppliers offer reasonable prices and quick delivery. Learning to create your own printed circuit boards will have rewarding benefits for your other technical hobbies.

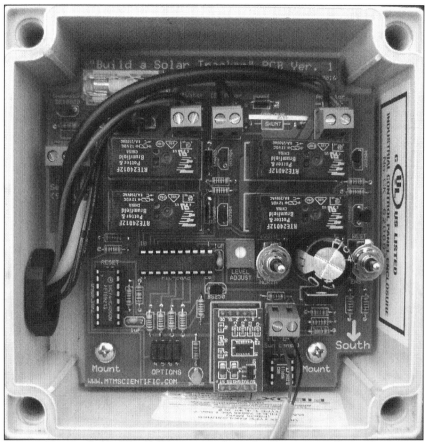

Figure 3-12. The PCB mounted inside the watertight enclosure.

Consider for example the company Expresspcb, LLC of Portland, Oregon. As a convenience to their customers, they offer free software for creating electrical circuit schematics. They also offer free software for designing printed circuit boards. By offering the free software they are hoping you will purchase your printed circuit boards from them.

The software programs from Expresspcb are simple to install, easy to use and effective for their intended purposes. In fact, all of the circuit diagrams and printed circuit boards in this book were created using their software. The software applications contain detailed instructions for use, and the application support is specifically designed to assist beginners.

You can become an effective user of their design software with only a few hours of dedicated study and practice.

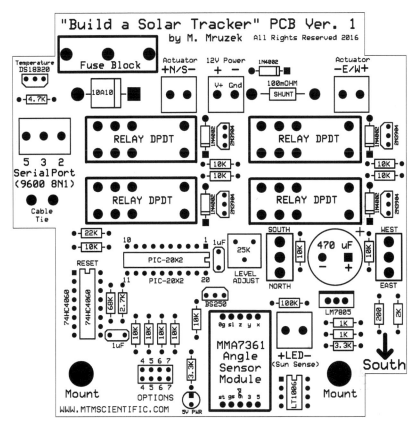

Figure 3-13. Printed Circuit Board (PCB) top view layout.

Here, we make a quick detour to say a few words in general about our PCB design philosophy. Modern electrical circuit components have become quite small in size, and certainly this is an advantage for most consumer electronic devices. However, these same small electronic components can create challenges when you are building circuits by hand. Fortunately, the popularity of electronics as a hobby has sustained an active market and ready supply of the more traditionally-sized components. The traditional electronic components are generally referred to as the "through-hole" type. This is in comparison to the more modern

49

"surface-mount" type, which are smaller and more difficult to place and solder on a printed circuit board. Figure 3-14 shows a comparison between a surface-mount resistor and a traditional through-hole resistor. Obviously, the larger through-hole components are easier to work with in a benchtop setting involving fabrication by hand.

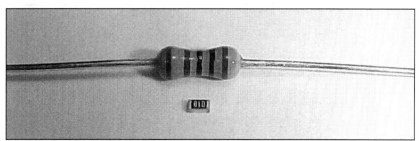

Figure 3-14. Comparison of traditional and surface-mount resistors.

The PCB for this project has been created as a two-sided board using traditional through-hole components. That means there are circuit traces on both the top and bottom of the board. Connections between the top and bottom layers are generally made at the same locations where the component leads pass through the board. In some situations, a circuit trace may need to pass from top to bottom through a special conductive pathway called a "via". A via is really nothing more than a plated-through hole in the PCB.

There is printed text and artwork on the top of the PCB to aid in indentifying and placing the various components. This is called the "silkscreen layer" because a silkscreen process was originally used to apply the artwork. Good design practice is to include useful and pertinent information on the silkscreen layer. The written information is an aid to anyone that might be examining the device in the field, such as for repair or troubleshooting.

The printed circuit board and all the electronic components required for assembly of the controller are shown in Figure 3-15. The assembled circuit board is shown in Figure 3-16. Notice that the PCB has an arrow to indicate the Southern direction, which is for proper mounting and setup on the tilt-tilt tracker frame. (We'll say more about tracker setup later.)

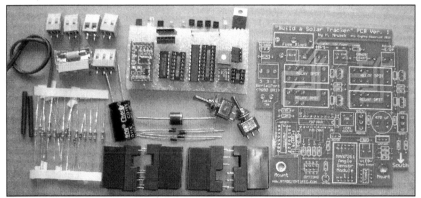

Figure 3-15. Electronic components required to build the controller.

Printed Circuit Board Assembly

Assembly of the circuit board is a process of carefully inserting and soldering each of the various electronic components into their proper locations. This is a part of the project that should be approached carefully, methodically, and with the correct tools, workspace and frame of mind. There is nothing more aggravating than soldering a component in the wrong location, or with the leads reversed. A mistaken component placement leaves you with the challenge of diagnosing the problem (later in the project), then attempting a tricky repair, and finally hoping everything works out okay after the repair work is finished.

Soldering is a simple and fun process, especially if you remember and implement the basic principles for success. We are going to put this as simply, and to the point, as possible:

1) Use a good quality temperature-controlled soldering iron.
2) Use a fine-pointed soldering tip that is clean, and kept clean.
3) Have a wet sponge handy for wiping the tip, and use it often.
4) Use an electronic-grade lead/tin solder with a non-corrosive flux.
5) Trim the wire leads after making a connection using side cutters.

Although it has become more common to use lead free solder for commercial electronics, we would suggest that (if possible) you consider using legacy lead-tin composition solder while learning to solder. The lead-tin solders are easier to work with for beginners, make a great looking connection and also start flowing at a lower temperature. The lower temperature translates to less risk of overheating heat-sensitive electronic parts.

Identifying individual electronic components is fairly easy; however some of the components do have a similar case style. In most cases you can double check the component's identity by examining the markings or labels on the device. Watch out especially for these components: The DS18B20 temperature sensor, BS250 FET transistor and 2N3904 NPN transistors. (They appear similar in general, but each has a distinctive case marking to aid with identification and assembly.)

There are several electronic components used in this circuit that must be assembled with a specific orientation. In other words, there is a right way and a wrong way to install the components. The right way to install the components is by using the telltale clues on the devices and on the PCB. The circuit board's artwork contains many helpful clues to guide you towards installing the electronic components correctly.

The components that you absolutely, positively must make sure to install correctly are the following:
1) Electrolytic Capacitor (470 uF)
2) Voltage Regulator (LM7805)
3) Transistors (2N3904, BS250)
4) Diodes (1N4002, LED, 10A10)
5) Integrated Circuits (PICAXE-20X2, LT1006, 74HC4060)
6) Temperature Sensor (DS18B20)
7) Accelerometer Module

Figure 3-16. View of assembled printed circuit board.

Let's examine each of these components in more detail to make sure we get it right.

The electrolytic capacitor is shown in Figure 3-17. The very first thing we might notice is that one of the wire leads is longer than the other. The longer lead must connect to the "+" terminal on the PCB. On the PCB this polarity is shown in two different ways. The first way is with a "+" sign on the artwork to show the correct lead location. The second way (and this is rather standard practice for layouts) is that the solder pad for the positive side is square rather than circular. You will also notice that the case of the capacitor is often marked with polarity information.

Figure 3-17. Capacitor, regulator and transistor PCB mounting.

The LM7805 voltage regulator is a three terminal device that could possibly be installed backwards. The key for correct placement is to note that the PCB artwork has a matching outline of the device's rear tab. Therefore, it's simply a matter of matching the physical case with the artwork outline, as shown in Figure 3-17.

In the same way, the transistors are correctly mounted by using their case outlines as a guide to match the artwork on the PCB. This is shown in detail in Figure 3-17. Notice how the flat side of the transistor matches the flat side of the artwork outline.

Diodes are also sensitive to reverse mounting. A standard system for indicating correct alignment for diode installation is used in the electronics industry. Most diodes have a distinctive band printed on their case. The band indicates correct placement end-for-end. If you look at the artwork on the PCB you will see the same band markings are also present there. Placing the diode correctly is simply a matter of aligning the band on the device to the band on the PCB artwork, as shown in Figure 3-18. Also, many multimeters have a diode polarity testing feature, which can be used if necessary.

Figure 3-18. Diode and LED mounting on PCB

There is an exception to the banding method of diode placement, and that is with the light emitting diodes (LED). The LED manufacturers have chosen to indicate polarity by making one wire lead longer than the other, as shown in Figure 3-18. For an LED, the longer lead is the "+" terminal. (This is identical to the identification system used for electrolytic capacitors.) The pad pattern for the LED "+" lead is indicated on the PCB with a square solder pad. In some cases, the LED will also have a notch on the side of the case as a visual cue for alignment with the PCB artwork.

The Sun sensor LED uses the same method for indicating polarity. When extending the Sun sensor leads with wire, make sure to note the polarity and correctly connect with the matching markings on the PCB, near the screw terminal connector. We suggest using wire with red insulation for the positive lead extension, and wire with black insulation for the negative lead extension.

The DS18B20 temperature sensor looks something like a transistor. Therefore, it is not surprising the same method of identifying lead placement is used. Simply match the flat on the sensor with the same flat on the artwork, as shown in Figure 3-19.

The accelerometer module has a dual set of male mounting pins on the bottom side of the device. We don't solder the module directly to the

PCB because it's designed to be replaceable. As shown in Figure 3-19, the module is attached to the printed circuit board using dual standoff headers. Notice that the text on the PCB artwork is similar to the text on the module, which will match when the module is installed correctly. Take care that you don't install the accelerometer module in reverse.

Figure 3-19. Accelerometer and temperature sensor PCB mounting.

We use several integrated circuits in this circuit, and one of the most common and destructive assembly mistakes is backwards installation. There are only two ways an IC can be mounted in a socket, but mounting the wrong way will usually damage the device. The most common method to indicate pin number "1" on an IC is with a small dot or indentation, as shown in Figure 3-20. Also, notice how the IC case has a notch on one end. That notch should agree with the identical notch on the PCB artwork, as shown in Figure 3-21. Additionally, you will find that the solder pad for pin "1" is square, while the other solder pads for the IC pins are round. All of the integrated circuits in this project are socketed, to facilitate easy replacement should that ever be necessary.

56

Figure 3-20. IC Pin #1 is marked at top left corner on these devices.

Resistor Identification

Numerous resistors are used in the solar tracker circuit, and it is important that the correct value resistor be installed in the correct PCB location. The best method to identify any resistor is by using a multimeter. This may seem like an expensive piece of test equipment to own, but even the most basic multimeter will suffice for this purpose. In Figure 3-22 we show a multimeter that was actually given-away for free at Harbor Freight when a coupon was presented at checkout. It's certainly a basic multimeter, but nevertheless it makes a great tool for measuring resistors. The multimeter can also be used for other parts of the project, such as measuring voltage levels.

Figure 3-21. The IC case-notch aligns with the artwork notch.

Without a multimeter, you may be tempted to identify resistors by decoding the color bands on the body of the component. For example, by using an online resistor calculator.

Using color-coded bands for resistor identification has a long history in electronics, dating back to a time when 5% tolerance resistors were a common industry standard. More recently, the metal film resistors have become more common because they cost approximately the same but have an improved 1% tolerance. Unfortunately, there are some differences in the color banding schemes for both, and combined with the blue body of the 1% resistors, it has become rather difficult to correctly identify some of the colors. It's actually pretty easy to get confused. That's why we strongly advise using a multimeter to identify all the resistors. Why take the chance?

Figure 3-22. Digital multimeter for checking resistor values.

Electrical Feedthrough

In this project the PCB is mounted inside a weatherproof enclosure box. The wiring to the PCB enters the enclosure through an electrical connector called a "feedthrough", as shown in Figure 3-23. The purpose of the feedthrough is to pass the wires into the enclosure in a manner that is weather and water tight. The feedthrough attaches to the enclosure using a threaded connector and plastic nut. The seal between the two parts is made with an O-ring.

The wires pass through the interior of the feedthrough, which consists of an elastomer insert, as shown in Figure 3-24. The elastomer is similar to rubber and forms a seal by gripping the insulation on the wire. The elastomer also provides some measure of strain relief to the wires, and minimizes damage to the electrical conductors inside. We have

mber for the feedthrough in the parts list. We chose a
ough to provide an opening for the optional serial cable.
: fourth hole with silicone sealant if you won't be using a
vo holes are used for the linear actuator cables, and one
: the power supply cable. Also, we should mention that the
holes in the insert tend to run on the smaller side, but they can be easily
drilled-out if any of your cables won't easily pass through.

Figure 3-23. Feedthrough for routing cables and wires to the PCB

Figure 3-24. The feedthrough has an elastomer insert for sealing.

Complete Circuit Schematic

Having examined the circuit schematic elements in detail, in Figure 3-26 we provide the complete electrical schematic for the dual axis solar tracker. One very important point to note regarding the circuit schematic is that we are making specific pin assignments for the PICAXE-20X2. The pin assignments determine which pins control which devices. This corresponds directly to the variable assignments we will be making in the software source code. In other words, the physical hardware and electrical circuit must agree with the corresponding variable assignments made in the software.

Complete Parts List

The complete parts list for populating the printed circuit board is provided in Figure 3-25. We have included part numbers from the original manufacturers, and also from suggested part suppliers. We have provided two references for the electronic parts to facilitate sourcing the parts from other suppliers. Most of the electrical parts are available directly from Digi-Key, Inc. The bare PCB can be purchased from MTM Scientific, Inc. MTM Scientific, Inc. also offers a complete kit with all the electronic parts, for a quick start on the project.

You may have an interest in studying the technical specifications of individual components in the parts list. A simple way to find manufacturer datasheets is by searching for the generic component name on a supplier's website (i.e. Digi-Key). The search will provide a page of relevant results, with hot links taking you directly to the full datasheets in PDF format.

Component Name	Qty	Manufacturer / Part Number	Supplier	Supplier Part Number / Notes
Picaxe-20X2 Microprocessor	1	Revolution Education, LLC.	phanderson.com	Must be programmed
Accelerometer Board	1	Various / Arduino Module	ebay.com	MMA7361 Active device
Printed Circuit Board (PCB)	1	MTM Scientific, Inc.	mtmscientific.com	Can be homebuilt
Current Shunt, 0.100 Ohm	1	Bourns, Inc. / PWR4412-2SDR1000F	digikey.com	PWR4412-2SDR1000F-ND
Relay DPDT	4	Axicom / RTE24012F	digikey.com	PB296-ND
Relay Socket	4	Axicom / RP78602	digikey.com	PB525-ND
Toggle Switch SPDT	2	E-Switch / 100SP1T1B1M1QEH	digikey.com	EG2350-ND
Fuse Holder, 5mm X 20mm	1	Littelfuse, Inc. / 0PTF015BP	digikey.com	F6245-ND
Fuse, 8A, Slow, 5mm X 20mm	1	Time-Delay Fuse (Type S505, GSF, 215)	mcmaster.com	#6986K641
LED, Yellow, T-1 3/4, 5mm, Round	1	Optek Technology / OV1FY3C7	digikey.com	365-1183-ND
LED, Red, T-1, 3mm, Round	1	Lite-On, Inc. / LTL-4261N	digikey.com	160-1035-ND
Double Terminal Block	4	AMP Connectors / 282836-2	digikey.com	A98076-ND
Triple Terminal Block	1	AMP Connectors / 282836-3	digikey.com	A98077-ND
NPN Transistor, 2N3904	4	Various / 2N3904 (Generic)	digikey.com	2N3904-APCT-ND
FET Transistor, BS250	1	Diodes Incorporated / BS250P	digikey.com	BS250P-ND
Capacitor, 1uF, 50V	2	Vishay / K105Z20Y5VF5TH5	digikey.com	BC1168CT-ND
Capacitor, 470uF, 100V	1	Nichicon / UVZ2A471MHD	digikey.com	493-1379-ND
Temperature Sensor	1	Maxim Integrated / DS18B20+	digikey.com	DS18B20+-ND
Diode, 1N4002, 100V, 1A	5	Fairchild Semiconductor / 1N4002	digikey.com	1N4002FSCT-ND
Diode, 10A10-B, 1000V, 10A	1	Rectron / 10A10-B	mouser.com	583-10A10-B / Polarity Reversal
IC, Counter, 74HC4060	1	Texas Instruments / SN74HC4060N	digikey.com	296-8209-5-ND
IC, Amplifier, LT1006	1	Linear Technology / LT1006CN8#PBF-ND	digikey.com	LT1006CN8#PBF-ND
IC, Regulator, LM7805	1	Fairchild Semiconductor / LM7805CT	digikey.com	LM7805CT-ND
Potentiometer, 25K	1	Bourns, Inc. / 3386F-1-253LF	digikey.com	3386F-253LF-ND
Resistor, 100K, 1/4W	1	Stackpole Electronics, Inc. / RNMF14FTC100K	digikey.com	S100KCACT-ND
Resistor, 68K, 1/4 W	1	Stackpole Electronics, Inc. / RNMF14FTC68K0	digikey.com	S68KCACT-ND
Resistor, 33K, 1/4W	2	Stackpole Electronics, Inc. / RNMF14FTC33K0	digikey.com	RNMF14FTC33K0CT-ND
Resistor, 10K	11	Stackpole Electronics, Inc. / RNMF14FTC10K0	digikey.com	S10KCACT-ND
Resistor, 4.7K	1	Stackpole Electronics, Inc. / RNMF14FTC4K70	digikey.com	S4.7KCACT-ND
Resistor, 3.3K	2	Stackpole Electronics, Inc. / RNMF14FTC3K30	digikey.com	S3.3KCACT-ND
Resistor, 2.7K	1	Stackpole Electronics, Inc. / RNMF14FTC2K70	digikey.com	S2.7KCACT-ND
Resistor, 2.0K	1	Stackpole Electronics, Inc. / RNMF14FTC2K00	digikey.com	S2KCACT-ND
Resistor, 1.0K	2	Stackpole Electronics, Inc. / RNMF14FTC1K00	digikey.com	S1KCACT-ND
Resistor, 200	1	Stackpole Electronics, Inc. / RNMF14FTC200R	digikey.com	S200CACT-ND
Socket, DIP, 20 Pin	1	Assmann WSW Components / A20-LC-TT	digikey.com	AE9998-ND
Socket, DIP, 16 Pin	1	Assmann WSW Components / A16-LC-TT	digikey.com	AE9992-ND
Socket, DIP, 8 Pin	1	Assmann WSW Components / A08-LC-TT	digikey.com	AE9986-ND
Header, 4 Pin, Double Row	1	FCI / 67997-108HLF	digikey.com	67997-108HLF
Jumpers (Option)	4	Sullins Connector Solutions / SPC02SYAN	digikey.com	S9001-ND
Headers	2	Sullins Connector Solutions / PPTC051LFBN-RC	digikey.com	S6103-ND

Figure 3-25. Complete parts list to populate the PCB.

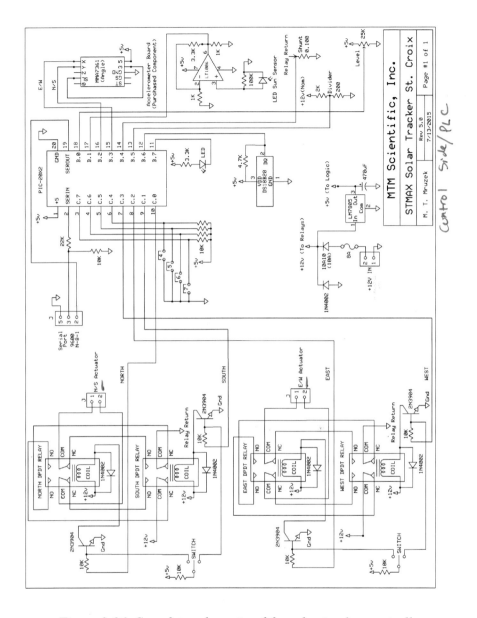

Figure 3-26. Complete schematic of the solar tracker controller.

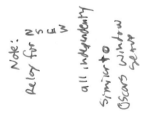

63

Chapter Four: Sensors

We have chosen to write a separate chapter on the topic of sensors, since multiple sensors are used for this project, and some of the sensor details are actually quite important to a successful project outcome. Here we describe sensors for measurement of sunlight, angle, temperature, current, and voltage. All the sensors we use have a voltage output that is proportional to the signal, except for the temperature sensor, which instead uses serial communication with the microcontroller.

Analog-to-Digital Conversion → Can do via PLC

The conversion of an analog signal, such as a voltage level, to a proportional integer number is the process of analog-to-digital conversion (ADC) or "A/D" for short. All of the measurements that we make in our solar tracker project will involve making an analog-to-digital conversion. Therefore, we are going to explain the A/D concept in detail.

The basic concept for all analog-to-digital converters is to start with a reference voltage. In our Picaxe project the reference voltage is the 5VDC power supply voltage supplied to the IC. That is one of the reasons we took care in the supply circuit to regulate the voltage precisely to 5.0 VDC using a linear LM7805 voltage regulator.

Analog-to-digital converters are rated by the number of bits they use to divide the reference voltage. On the PICAXE-20X2 we have the option of doing an 8 bit or 10 bit conversion. The 8 bit conversion will divide the reference voltage into 256 steps, and the 10 bit conversion will divide the reference voltage into 1024 steps. Obviously, the 10 bit conversion has smaller voltage steps and a finer resolution, and it is generally our preferred approach for making sensor measurements.

We can calculate the precise step levels for a 10 bit conversion. If the reference voltage is 5.0 VDC and we divide that into 1024 steps, each step will be 5.0 / 1024 = 0.004883 Volts per step (4.883 mV per step). Roughly speaking then, we have about 5 millivolt resolution per step.

8 bit = 256 steps

65 preferred = 10 bits = 1024 " "

Let's do an example calculation. Suppose we are told that an A/D converter is doing a 10 bit conversion with a 5VDC reference voltage and reports the integer number 338. What is the corresponding voltage it's measuring? The answer is simply 338 x 0.004883 = 1.650 VDC.

The Picaxe microcontroller has a total of eleven analog-to-digital converters. Each A/D converter is associated with a different input pin. All of the A/D converters are designed for measuring voltage signals. The general data acquisition approach, therefore, is to select the appropriate sensors capable of converting our measurement of interest into a voltage signal. That's because sensors with voltage outputs are suitable for the A/D converters on the Picaxe microcontroller.

One more important point about A/D conversion: A single A/D conversion will always be subject to the possibility of electrical noise in the signal, as well as some natural variation in the signal for physical reasons. Fortunately, those issues are easily addressed by taking multiple A/D readings and averaging the result. When you examine the source code for the tracker software program, you will see that whenever any A/D conversion is made we always acquire multiple readings and calculate an average. The Picaxe microcontroller can acquire the A/D readings, perform the mathematical averaging, and report the final result very quickly.

Sunlight Sensors

We begin with a discussion of the Sun sensor. The sensor we have developed for this dual axis solar tracker project represents a large investment of time and effort to perfect. We will be describing the Sun sensor in detail because it is not available directly off the shelf. The Sun sensor is not difficult to construct, and we will provide instructions and directions for doing so later in this chapter.

But first, what are the characteristics of an ideal sensor for solar trackers? Well, we can start with some of the basics: Inexpensive, reliable and uniform output are some desirable traits. We also want the output signal response to be highest when aiming directly at the Sun. We show a graphical representation of desirable Sun sensor response in Figure 4-1.

A great deal of time was spent investigating Sun sensors, and it may be helpful to mention a few approaches that don't work. This examination will help convey some of the noteworthy aspects of the sensor we eventually chose to use in this project.

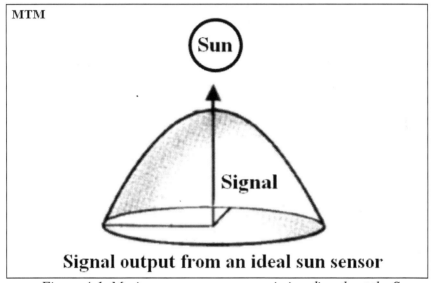

Signal output from an ideal sun sensor

Figure 4-1. Maximum sensor response aiming directly at the Sun.

Consider a simple solar cell as a Sun sensor, as shown in Figure 4-2. These cells produce an electrical voltage when exposed to sunlight, and they are available in conveniently small sizes. They are also inexpensive and reliable. They would seem to be the ideal sensor from both those perspectives. Indeed, when we measure the signal output of a solar cell when swept from side to side, with the Sun in the middle, we get a very reasonable-looking response curve, as shown in Figure 4-3.

But, let's take a closer look at the response curve of the solar cell in greater detail. Yes, we see that the response does peak when aimed directly at the Sun, but note how the peak is not sharp. In fact, the response is rather muted when aimed directly at the Sun, with the output signal varying by only a few percent points over a wide-angle range of perhaps 30 or 40 degrees. This is not the type of response which is desirable if we want to locate the Sun's position within a few degrees of accuracy. We do want a sensor that has a wide angular range, but we also want a sharp definite response peak when aiming directly at the Sun.

Figure 4-2. A small solar cell for detecting sunlight.

Another type of sensor which has been quite popular with various solar trackers is the simple light emitting diode (LED). These sensors have the great advantage of being inexpensive and fairly sensitive to sunlight and are packaged for rough use. The typical LED has a small active area near the bottom of the plastic case. The active area responds to sunlight by producing a voltage signal.

We experimented with many different styles and types of LED sensors and found that one of the most suitable is a simple 5 mm size (T-1 3/4), designed to produce yellow light, with a clear plastic encasement. There was only one problem with the stock LED types: We found that they are unpredictably sensitive to off-axis sunlight. In other words they suffered from "false peaks" due to internal reflections created by sideways-sunlight impinging on the active area.

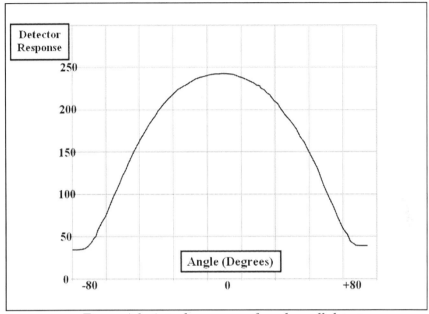

Figure 4-3. Actual response of a solar cell detector

We subsequently found that variations in the off-axis sunlight sensitivity could be smoothed by modifying the basic LED sensor with a simple cosmetic process. We found that by scuffing the case of the LED housing using an abrasive pad (Scotchbrite®) we could reduce the variability of the side reflections, and create a sensor optimized for precise Sun position sensing, as shown in Figure 4-4 and Figure 4-5. The response of such a sensor is shown in Figure 4-6. Note that we have used nearly identical graphical scaling compared to Figure 4-3, such that the difference in the sensitivity towards the direction of the Sun is clearly evident. Equally important, the sensor also exhibits an inclined signal response moving towards the Sun position, even when aimed from a large angular distance away from the actual peak. That means the sensor is capable of determining which direction represents moving closer to the Sun. In technical jargon the LED sensor has a wide "field of view".

Figure 4-4. Abrasive scuffing of the LED improves performance.

Figure 4-5. Comparison of original LED and scuffed LED.

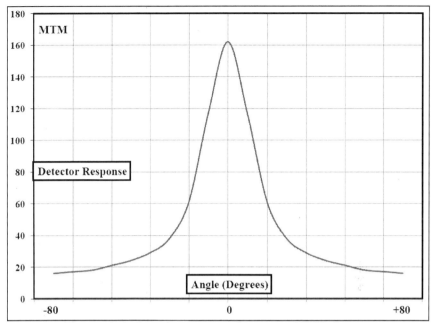

Figure 4-6. Actual response of improved LED Sun sensor.

Another important consideration concerning the use of an LED sensor is that the signal must be slightly amplified and buffered for reliable operation. The signal from the LED is conditioned with an amplifier IC, before routing to the analog-to-digital converter on the Picaxe. We found this buffering circuit is necessary to create a repeatable signal level from the LED sensor.

The LED sensor amplifier circuit is shown in Figure 4-7. The active device is the LT1006, which is a precision single-supply operational amplifier. This particular device works well on a single 5VDC supply. The circuit voltage gain of 4.3X is set by the feedback resistance divider. We chose the gain to keep the signal in the working range of the A/D converter of the Picaxe.

The LED light sensor must be mounted on the payload platform, preferably near the circuit board's screw terminal connector. Extend the wire leads of the LED sensor using ordinary wire, ideally red colored wire for the positive lead and black colored wire for the negative lead. Use two short lengths of shrink tubing to insulate the soldered wire connections. We mount the LED sensor centrally in the top lid of the enclosure. This can be accomplished by drilling a 13/64" diameter hole in the cover, inserting the LED sensor, and sealing the installation with a dab of silicone sealant. Such a mount is shown in Figure 4-9. This mounting method also helps to reduce the possibility of sunlight entering the LED from the side, since the enclosure's lid has a finite thickness.

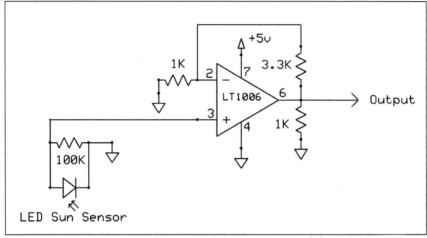

Figure 4-7. Circuit diagram of Sun sensor amplifier. (Gain=4.3X)

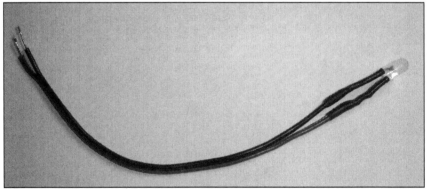

Figure 4-8. LED sensor with a pair of wire leads attached.

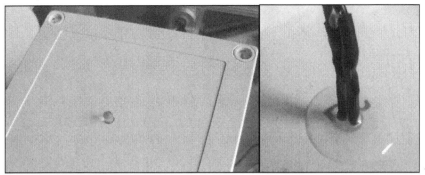

Figure 4-9. Mount the sensor in the top lid of the enclosure.

Current Sensor

Measuring the direct current amperage flow in the solar tracker controller circuit is useful in our design for several reasons. We use the current measurement to determine if a linear actuator has hit a limit switch (Current ≈ 0 Amps), or if the tracker hardware has hit an obstruction or other obstacle (Current ≥ 2 Amps).

Figure 4-10. A standard current shunt and a miniature shunt.

Measuring DC current is fairly easy if we convert the current flow to a proportional voltage signal. That's because we can measure the voltage signal using an A/D converter on the Picaxe microcontroller.

We use a device called a "shunt" to measure current, as shown in Figure 4-10. A shunt is really nothing more than a resistor. The resistance is sufficiently small such that the shunt can be inserted into the main power path of the circuit, without detriment to the operation of the remainder of the circuit. In this project, we use a shunt resistor of 0.100 ohms resistance. The shunt is placed in the ground return path of the main power supply circuit. With the chosen shunt, a load current of 1 ampere will create a voltage signal of 0.100 volts, or 100 millivolts.

Temperature Sensor

The measurement of temperature is potentially useful for building and operating the dual axis solar controller. Since the enclosure box for the solar tracker controller will be mounted on the payload platform, and because the box will be in direct sunlight, we have an interest in knowing the temperature inside the enclosure box.

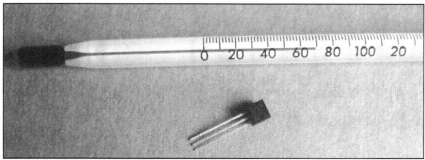

Figure 4-11. Simple IC performs the function of a thermometer.

The sensor used for measuring temperature is the DS18B20, as shown in Figure 4-11. This small device is really quite amazing for its capability. The three terminal package, which looks rather like a

74

transistor, is actually a calibrated temperature sensor with built-in linearization, and the ability to communicate with the Picaxe microcontroller using a communication protocol known as the 1-Wire® interface. For our purposes, we don't need to know much more about the internal workings of this sensor, although there is much more information available in the device's datasheet if you would like to know more. Suffice to say, we can directly connect the sensor to the Picaxe and read temperature with a simple software command. We use the sensor for reading temperatures in the range of 0 to 127 degrees C. The temperature measurement circuit is shown in Figure 4-12.

Voltage Sensor

Measuring the main power supply voltage provided to the solar tracker controller provides potentially useful information. For example, since the solar tracker may be operating from a battery, we might monitor the general charge condition of the battery. In this example, if the battery begins to discharge past a safe voltage level we could instruct the tracker to cease operations and move to the park position, to preserve power. Another option might be to monitor the power supply voltage when a linear actuator is moving, to look for long term trends related to linear actuator operation.

Since the power supply to the solar tracker controller can range upwards to 12VDC or more, and since the maximum input voltage of the analog-to-digital converters on the Picaxe is only 5VDC, we need a buffer circuit. With a buffer circuit we use some additional components to create a voltage signal which is proportional to the supply signal, but is still within the allowable range of the ADC. This conditioning of the signal is accomplished by using a circuit called a "voltage divider" as shown in Figure 4-13. The output of the voltage divider is a signal which is proportional to the input signal, merely reduced by exactly a factor of eleven.

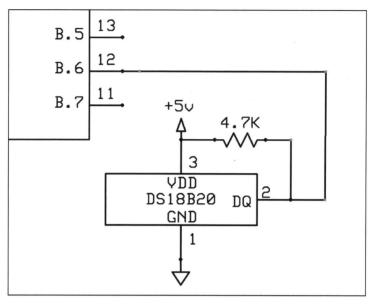

Figure 4-12. Temperature sensor connection to a PICAXE-20X2.

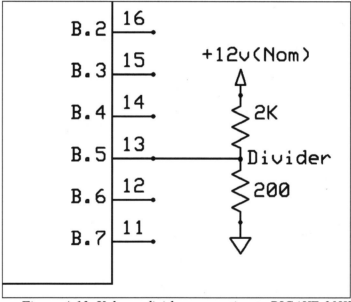

Figure 4-13. Voltage divider connection to PICAXE-20X2.

Angle Sensors

In this book we define angle measurements of the solar tracker payload platform position by using the local horizon as the definition of "level". (Speaking mathematically: The level direction is perpendicular to the local gravity vector.) Electronically measuring the angle of an object with respect to level has evolved from being a very difficult measurement, to being a very simple measurement, in the course of only a few years' time. This is due to the amazing advancements that have been made in the technology known as "MEMS", which stands for Micro-Electro-Mechanical Systems.

Figure 4-14. Accelerometer used for tilt-tilt angle measurement.

Modular MEMS angle sensors are widely available from numerous suppliers, and they can even be found on Ebay. The common active element for these angle sensor modules is the MMA7361 manufactured by Freescale Semiconductor in Tempe, Arizona. These modules are often mentioned in regard to applications using the Arduino microcontroller. Although the active MMA7361 element can be purchased separately, it really is much more practical to purchase and use a complete angle sensing module, as shown in Figure 4-14. The cost of a ready-to-use module is only a few dollars, and the module is easily replaced, if there should ever be a need. The active element inside the sensor is a micromachined mechanical beam structure which deflects as it is moved and rotated in a gravitational field. The interior deflections are measured using a capacitive technique, and the resulting electrical signal is conditioned with an internal amplifier and buffer circuit. If you are interested in knowing more about the internal workings of the MMA7361 active element, there is much more information available in the manufacturer's datasheets and application notes.

The angle sensor module is designed to measure angles in 3 orthogonal directions; however we use only two of the directions: X & Y. The X channel is used to measure the East-West tilt angle, and the Y channel is used to measure the North-South tilt angle. The output of the module for both the channels is a voltage signal proportional to angle. The voltage signal is sent to the Picaxe, where an analog-to-digital converter reads the signal and reports the result in ADC count units, as shown in Figure 4-17. It is not necessary for us to convert the ADC counts to angular degrees. Instead, we find it's easier and more convenient to work directly with the signal in the native ADC units, as reported by the Picaxe.

When the payload platform of the dual axis solar tracker is level, both the East-West and North-South position reports are reported as 338 ADC counts. The Park position for the solar tracker is with the East-West tilt at level, and the North-South tilt aimed toward the horizon at a 45 degree angle. In that case, the position is reported as North-South = 455 ADC counts and East-West = 338 ADC counts. Note that the North-South ADC counts increase as the tilt axis moves Southward.

Theoretical Output of MMA7361 Sensor with 5VDC Supply & 1.5G Range Setting					
North-South Angle	East-West Angle	North-South V	East-West V	North-South ADC	East-West ADC
Level	Level	1.65	1.65	338	338
Level	45 East	1.65	1.08	338	221
Level	45 West	1.65	2.22	338	455
45 South	Level	2.22	1.65	455	338
45 South	45 East	2.22	1.08	455	255
45 South	45 West	2.22	2.22	455	421

Figure 4-15. Lookup table for ADC counts from the angle sensor.

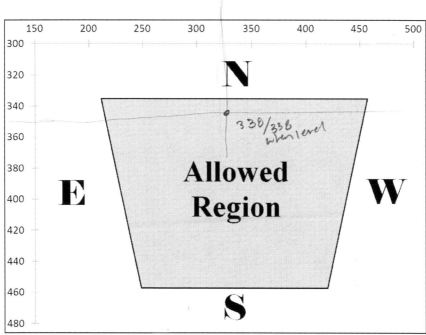

Figure 4-16. Map of allowed tilt locations, in ADC count units.

A lookup table for understanding the ADC count numbers for indicating tilt angles is shown in Figure 4-15. The important takeaway is that the numbers we use to represent angular positions can be in arbitrary ADC units, so long as the measurements are consistent from movement to movement, and also from device to device. This is indeed the case.

The tilt angle data in the table can be plotted to create a "map" of angle space where the tracker moves, as shown in Figure 4-16. Note that the signal response has a keystone shape. The East-West sensitivity is reduced as the payload platform moves Southward from the level position.

We actually use the angle space map to do error checking in the software. In normal operation, the tracker position reports should always be inside the allowed space map. A reading outside the allowed space might indicate something unexpected has happened. In effect, we can use the angle space map to make virtual limit switches, as described in the next section.

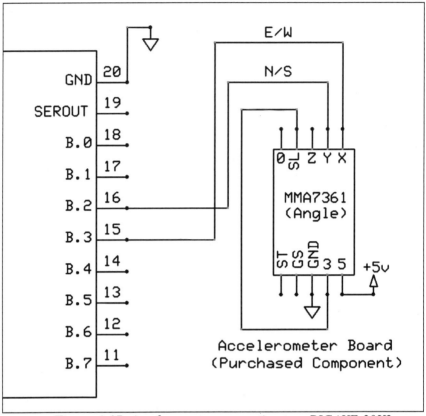

Figure 4-17. Accelerometer connection to a PICAXE-20X2.

Limit Switches

Readers who are familiar with building solar trackers, whether they are single axis or dual axis, may be familiar with the practice of incorporating limit switches to control the range of motion of the solar tracker hardware. Limit switches are present in this solar tracker design, in the sense that we are using the limit switches which are already included inside the linear actuators. The mechanical range of motion of the tracker hardware coincides with the range of motion of the linear actuators.

However, because we have included a dual axis angle measurement system for sensing the directional aim of the solar tracker, we can leverage that angular position information to add some useful safety features to our design.

Referring back to Figure 4-16, we see a map of ADC counts for the East-West and North-South motion as the tracker changes position. In effect, we have a map of "allowed" motion space. We can certainly use that position information in our software code to verify the solar tracker is always working in the correct angle motion space.

What are some examples of why that might not be occurring? Well, consider what would happen if the wind happened to blow over the solar tracker frame. At that point, how would the software know that something is wrong and to stop moving? The solution is to include a simple limit test on the ADC position readings, such that we verify the readings are in the allowed space before any movement is initiated. Incidentally, this feature was added after that very event happened during the development of the solar tracker! This safety check is the purpose of the subroutine called "Range_Check" in the software code.

Just one more comment about limit switches: If for some reason you would like to include a limit switch, or any type of switch for that matter, you might consider using the option jumper inputs, as described in the next section. Of course, modification of the software would also be required to make the additional switches functional.

Option Jumpers

When a device is controlled by a microcontroller it may be desirable to change the operational behavior of the system, without the requirement to modify and reprogram the software. By making proper provisions in the software beforehand, variations in tracker operation can simply be selected by configuring option jumpers after the fact.

The ability to easily change or adjust solar tracker operational behavior is the purpose of the option jumpers. There are four option jumpers available on the PCB. Two of the option jumpers have assigned dedicated functions in the baseline design, while the other two option jumpers are available for your future use.

The two option jumpers which have been programmed with specific purposes in the existing solar tracker software are as follows:

Jumper 4: This option jumper has been programmed as a "timer" jumper. If option jumper 4 is present, the solar tracker controller only makes aiming adjustments every 30 minutes, instead of every six minutes.

Jumper 5: This option jumper has been programmed to set up the solar tracker controller for operation in the Southern Hemisphere. If option jumper 5 is present, the controller tracks the Sun by moving in the opposite direction.

Two of the option jumpers are not used in the existing software program: Jumpers 6 & 7. These two jumpers are available for potential new uses, based on your ideas and interest.

The circuit diagram for the wiring of the option jumpers is shown in Figure 4-18. In most cases, option jumpers are not installed.

Potentiometer: Level Adjust

We have included a small adjustable potentiometer on the PCB. The potentiometer is for your future use. The potentiometer provides a convenient method of "dialing-in" an adjustable input level setting. Presently, the software does not use the input level setting for any dedicated purpose. You can read the level setting of the potentiometer when the tracker is operating by using the software's manual mode.

The potentiometer level setting is read and stored as a byte variable. In other words, the valid range is from 0 to 255. The potentiometer provides a convenient method for making field adjustments to an optional software parameter. For example, you could program the potentiometer reading to adjust an operating variable, such as the minimum sunlight level "Full_Sun". The potentiometer is shown in Figure 4-19. In practice, the potentiometer is easily adjusted by using a small flat blade screwdriver.

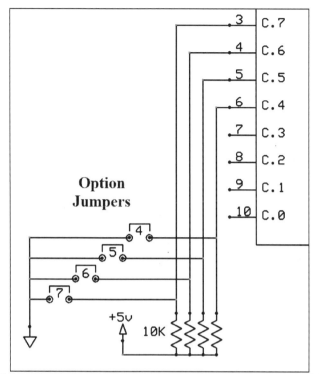

Figure 4-18. Option jumpers connection to the PICAXE-20X2.

Figure 4-19. Level adjust potentiometer on the PCB.

Chapter Five: Picaxe Microcontroller

In this chapter, we present detailed information about the Picaxe microcontroller. The Picaxe memory organization is important to understand because memory space is limited. The Picaxe memory must be used efficiently. Also in this chapter, we describe the serial communication features of the Picaxe and build a simple setup to test our associated development tools. The working details of serial communication are discussed in this chapter. Programming the Picaxe requires the use of serial communication, and that's also how we communicate with the solar tracker controller while it is operating.

The microcontroller used in this project is called a PICAXE-20X2. This device is, for all intents and purposes, a small computer. As you might expect, the number of options and the specific details of operation have the potential to become very complex. We are going to focus on the "big picture" using the PICAXE-20X2, while still providing enough detail for you to modify the project for your own purposes going forward.

PICAXE-20X2

+5V	1	20	Ground
(Serial In)	2	19	A.0 (Serial Out)
(ADC3/Out/In) C.7	3	18	B.0 (In/Out/ADC1)
(In) C.6	4	17	B.1 (In/Out/ADC2)
(Out/In) C.5	5	16	B.2 (In/Out/ADC4)
(Out/In) C.4	6	15	B.3 (In/Out/ADC5)
(ADC7/Out/In) C.3	7	14	B.4 (In/Out/ADC6)
(ADC8/Out/In) C.2	8	13	B.5 (In/Out/ADC10)
(ADC9/Out/In) C.1	9	12	B.6 (In/Out/ADC11)
(Out/In) C.0	10	11	B.7 (In / Out)

Figure 5-1. Pinout for the PICAXE-20X2 used in this project.

The pinout for the Picaxe microcontroller is shown in Figure 5-1. Two pins are reserved for the 5VDC power supply and ground connections. Two more pins are reserved for the serial communication input and output (I/O) connections. The balance of the pins are multipurpose, and they can each be individually configured per the options listed for the specific pin. An efficient project strategy is to use the digital pins for simple I/O, and to use the ADC pins for physical measurements. Also, it is important to know that these pins must be configured in the software code. You will find the pin configuration commands in the source code as part of the "Initialization" subroutine.

Building this dual axis solar tracker requires the use of a Picaxe microcontroller which has been programmed with the solar tracker controller source code. If you decide to do the programming yourself, it's relatively easy to accomplish. The software application for programming the Picaxe is available free of charge from Revolution Education, Ltd. A nice feature of the Picaxe devices is that you don't need a special IC programming machine. The Picaxe can be programmed using an RS-232 serial connection combined with a few simple circuit components. The same serial connection used for programming can also be used to communicate with the solar tracker controller while it's operating.

The software programmed into the microcontroller is stored in non-volatile memory. That means the controller program is not erased when the power is removed. It also means you must reprogram the Picaxe if you want to change anything regarding the solar tracker software.

The Picaxe operating system uses variables of different sizes. Flags are single "bit" variables which are either true (1) or false (0). Larger in size, "byte" variables consist of eight bits. The byte variable has a valid range of zero to 255. Even larger in size, the "word" variable consists of 16 bits. The word variable has a valid range of zero to 65535. The Picaxe variables are summarized in Figure 5-2.

It is important to know and remember that the Picaxe microcontroller is only capable of performing integer math. The Picaxe microcontroller is not able to do math calculations with decimal numbers or with

86

negative numbers. All Picaxe math calculations must be performed using variables which represent positive integers. The requirement to use integer math is one of the most important characteristics with respect to writing software source code for the Picaxe microcontroller. The requirement to perform all of our math calculations using positive integers is not much of a limitation. In fact, it turns out to be very easy to accomplish all of our computational goals using only integer math.

Variable Sizes, Ranges and Typical Uses for STMAX			
Variable	Size	Valid Range	Generally Used For:
Bit	1 Bit	0-1	Logical Flags, Option Jumpers, etc.
Byte	8 Bits	0-255	8 bit ADC Readings
Word	16 Bits	0-65535	All 10 bit ADC Readings

Figure 5-2. Variable declarations match the data memory required.

The Picaxe microcontroller is capable of performing analog-to-digital (A/D) conversions. That means the microcontroller can read a sensor input, such as a voltage level, and convert the reading to a proportional integer. The A/D converter in the microcontroller can perform 8 bit conversions, and also 10 bit conversions for increased accuracy. In this project we generally perform A/D conversions with 10 bits of accuracy.

Since a 10 bit number is too large for a byte variable (8 bits), we must use a word variable for storing the data. As you will recall, a word variable can store up to a 16 bit number.

The Picaxe microcontroller has the built-in ability to perform RS-232 serial communication. Most modern computers today use USB communication, which stands for "Universal Serial Bus". The USB communication protocol does have some advantages: higher speed, automatic device recognition and miniaturized connectors, to name a few.

From our project perspective RS-232 serial communication has some important advantages over USB communication. For example, RS-232 serial communication has good immunity to electrical noise, which is especially important for field operations. Also, RS-232 has a simple connector interface that is compatible with hand soldering. Another advantage of RS-232 is the ability to make long cable runs. Finally, RS-232 serial communication has a long history with computers so there are many free software programs available for communication using the protocol.

Picaxe Memory Organization

The memory organization of the Picaxe microcontroller can quickly become complicated. That's because the PICAXE-20X2 microcontroller device is a standard PIC (Programmable Instruction Controller) to which has been added the Picaxe boot-loading code, as written by Revolution Education, Ltd. The boot code adds the Picaxe BASIC operating system and also creates an internal memory organization to operate the microcontroller. In operation, the Picaxe microcontroller executes the logical instructions we provide with our software source code.

In this project, we focus on describing the memory organization as provided by the Picaxe operating system, since that is the operating system we are using. From the viewpoint of the Picaxe operating system, we can pretty easily describe what is and is not allowed.

The PICAXE-20X2 is organized as follows: 56 bytes for variables, 4096 bytes for the program, and 256 bytes for non-volatile data storage. Now, there are all sorts of tricks and techniques to modify and work around these settings. However, if we just keep to the basics, that's basically what we have to work with in an off-the-shelf PICAXE-20X2. Fortunately, our dual axis tracker project works great with this basic memory structure.

Understanding the intricate details of the Picaxe memory organization is important only if you decide to modify the controller program in the future. In that case, you may decide to reuse or reassign memory space for your own purposes. More commonly, we expect you may only have an interest in "tweaking" some of the logical commands or settings in the source code, in which case the memory organization likely won't need to be changed at all.

Variable Space

The PICAXE-20X2 memory organization provides 56 bytes of space for general purpose variables. The first byte is automatically labeled B0, the second byte is labeled B1, the third byte is labeled B2, etc. The last byte is labeled B55. As you will recall, a byte is 8 bits of data. Two bytes can be combined to make a word, which is 16 bits of data.

The same 56 bytes of space for general purpose variables can be described several other ways, all of which are equivalent. Since a word variable consists of 2 bytes, the 56 byte space can also be described as containing room for 28 words. Also, since a byte can be described as 8 bits, the same 56 bytes can be described as containing space for 448 bits.

The equivalence of the nomenclature for the same variable space is shown in Figure 5-3. Bytes 0 and 1 are the same as bits 0 to 15, which are the same as word 0. In the same way, bytes 2 and 3 are the same as bits 16 to 31, which are the same as word 1. Note that the variable numbering scheme always starts with a zero.

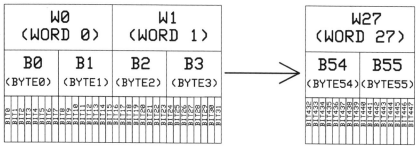

Figure 5-3. Memory space allocation for variables in PICAXE-20X2.

Why do we use bits, bytes and words to store information in our variables? That's a good question. Consider the simple example of storing a single piece of information about the "state" of something. That is to say, whether the state is "True" or "False". In that case a bit variable is the ideal way to store the information because it has only two states: "True"=1 or "False"=0.

Suppose we want to store a piece of information which is an integer number with a maximum value of 255. Well, in that case a byte variable is ideal because it can range anywhere from 0 up to 255.

In the same way, suppose we want to store a piece of information that is an integer number with a maximum value of 65535. In that case, a word variable is ideal because it can range anywhere from 0 up to 65535.

The bottom line is that we want to assign variable space to hold information according to the size of the information. Of course, we can always store a small number in a large variable space, but doing so wastes some of the memory space. In a microcontroller, the memory space is limited and we don't want to waste it.

The variable space allocations for our solar tracker software program are made in the source code, which is provided in the appendix. Variable declarations are one of the first tasks of writing a computer program. Upon examination you will find that the variable declarations are at the beginning of the program. Our computer program uses all of the available memory space for making variable assignments. Some of the memory space is used for bit variables, some is used for byte variables, and the balance is used for word variables.

Program Space

The Picaxe memory organization provides 4096 bytes for the program space. The program space is where we load the operating instructions for what the program actually "does". The program is a long text file containing sequential logical instructions, one line after the other. The program text file is called the "source code" listing. You can read and follow the source code text file to understand the logical progression of the software flow. The complete source code for the solar tracker program is listed in the appendix.

The Picaxe provides 4096 bytes of space for the program and we use much of it for this project. However, there remains enough space available for additional minor changes and modifications, if desired. It is important to remember that when a program is downloaded to the Picaxe, it will remain in the device after the power is turned "OFF". When starting with a brand new PICAXE-20X2, you must first load a software program into the device to begin useful operation. After loading, the program will remain in memory indefinitely, until the device is loaded with something different.

Non-Volatile Data Storage

The non-volatile data storage area of the Picaxe memory space is where we store data for future use. This data storage area is safe because the information is not lost if the power to the Picaxe is lost or removed. In this project we store information in the non-volatile data storage area about the time and position of the Sun. Afterwards, when doing a sky search to look for the Sun, we can use this position information to aim the solar tracker and achieve a quicker start. In the program source code we call the process of using the stored Sun position data a "Warm Start".

The non-volatile data storage area is used to store information about the time and position of the Sun. We want to record the time, and the two tilt angles. (East-West and North-South). The information is stored in a one-dimensional linear matrix array, which is basically a fancy way of saying a long list. We use the solar time as an index for where to store the data in the matrix, or list. The non-volatile data storage area is initially completely filled with zeroes. The stored data only changes when we write to the area during normal tracker operations.

The non-volatile data organization is shown in Figure 5-4. Each data set for a position "fix" of the Sun is allocated 5 bytes. The East-West and North-South position variables are each 2 bytes each. That means one byte per data block is not used, and therefore the space remains available for future use. Notice that we use the time variable as an index for where the position data is stored in the array.

91

A total of 5 bytes of data space is allocated per data set. There are 48 data sets. (There are two data sets per hour.) That is a total of 240 bytes allocated. Since the non-volatile data storage area size is 256 bytes, there remain 16 bytes of space that are free and available. Those 16 bytes of memory space are available at the end of the non-volatile data storage area. The empty space at the end of the non-volatile storage area could be used for other purposes in the future, such as storing additional data related to solar tracker operation.

System Memory

There is another place that a small amount of information can be stored in memory in a PICAXE-20X2: System Memory. This minor memory storage area has been set aside for system variable use by the manufacturer. However, in our application all the system memory is not being used by the system and we have used some of it for our own purposes instead.

We decided to use the available system memory for three additional variables. This decision was made after the main program had been written. We had an interest in knowing the running total of "Mini_Sky" Searches, "Full_Sky" Searches and "Tracks". (All of these operations are done by the solar tracker during the course of a day.) For that reason, we created corresponding variables in system memory during the variable declaration section of the code. You will see the assignments in the "Initialize" portion of the code. We have used all the memory space that was available in that area. No additional space is available there now.

Project Computer

As you might expect, this project uses a computer. So, let's briefly discuss some of the considerations in regard to selecting a project computer. Now, your first inclination might be to use a computer which you already have available... possibly the "family" computer somewhere around the home. Another thought might be to try to adapt a small handheld device, such as a tablet or phone, for this project. Although every situation is different, we'd like to suggest that you consider purchasing and dedicating a computer especially for this project.

Not only will you be doing hardware and software development with the computer, you will also be using it in the field when the solar tracker becomes operational. In addition, the easiest method to communicate with and program the Picaxe microcontroller is with good, old-fashioned RS-232 serial communication using a nine pin serial port connector. However, most new computers today don't have a nine pin serial port. Today, most new computers have a USB type serial port instead.

Here is our suggested course of action: obtain, purchase or refurbish an old computer specifically for this project. For example, consider the lowly laptop, as shown in Figure 5-5. A simple search on Ebay will turn-up literally tens of thousands of used laptops for sale, with many at practically giveaway prices. In addition, many of those older laptops have a built-in nine pin serial port.

Acquiring and using an old laptop actually solves several problems at once: You will have a dedicated-use computer for the project, the computer is easily portable, the computer has a display, the computer can operate on battery power, the computer can run the software we plan to use, and the computer has a built-in means of communication with our project hardware. All this in a device which can easily be found for less than $50. It is even possible that you may already have one, or know someone that will give you such a computer for free. Similar computers can often be found at yard sales or even at second hand thrift stores.

Although many laptop computers will work in this application, we can suggest a few common models that work well and are readily available on Ebay. For example, this book was typed on a Dell Latitude D530 laptop computer. We purchased this computer on Ebay, postage paid for $35. It came preloaded with Windows XP, which although an older operating system, is stable and capable. Another model to consider might be a Dell Latitude D600, which not only has a serial port, but is the last laptop model from Dell that has a good old-fashioned printer port.

00:00 N/S	00:00 E/W	Byte 5	00:30 N/S	00:30 E/W	Byte 10
01:00 N/S	01:00 E/W	Byte 15	01:30 N/S	01:30 E/W	Byte 20
02:00 N/S	02:00 E/W	Byte 25	02:30 N/S	02:30 E/W	Byte 30
03:00 N/S	03:00 E/W	Byte 35	3:30 N/S	03:30 E/W	Byte 40
04:00 N/S	04:00 E/W	Byte 45	4:30 N/S	04:30 E/W	Byte 50
05:00 N/S	05:00 E/W	Byte 55	5:30 N/S	05:30 E/W	Byte 60
06:00 N/S	06:00 E/W	Byte 65	6:30 N/S	06:30 E/W	Byte 70
07:00 N/S	07:00 E/W	Byte 75	7:30 N/S	07:30 E/W	Byte 80
08:00 N/S	08:00 E/W	Byte 85	8:30 N/S	08:30 E/W	Byte 90
09:00 N/S	09:00 E/W	Byte 95	9:30 N/S	09:30 E/W	Byte 100
10:00 N/S	10:00 E/W	Byte 105	10:30 N/S	10:30 E/W	Byte 110
11:00 N/S	11:00 E/W	Byte 115	11:30 N/S	11:30 E/W	Byte 120
12:00 N/S Solar Noon	**12:00 E/W** Solar Noon	Byte 125	12:30 N/S	12:30 E/W	Byte 130
13:00 N/S	13:00 E/W	Byte 135	13:30 N/S	13:30 E/W	Byte 140
14:00 N/S	14:00 E/W	Byte 145	14:30 N/S	14:30 E/W	Byte 150
15:00 N/S	15:00 E/W	Byte 155	15:30 N/S	15:30 E/W	Byte 160
16:00 N/S	16:00 E/W	Byte 165	16:30 N/S	16:30 E/W	Byte 170
17:00 N/S	17:00 E/W	Byte 175	17:30 N/S	17:30 E/W	Byte 180
18:00 N/S	18:00 E/W	Byte 185	18:30 N/S	18:30 E/W	Byte 190
19:00 N/S	19:00 E/W	Byte 195	19:30 N/S	19:30 E/W	Byte 200
20:00 N/S	20:00 E/W	Byte 205	20:30 N/S	20:30 E/W	Byte 210
21:00 N/S	21:00 E/W	Byte 215	21:30 N/S	21:30 E/W	Byte 220
22:00 N/S	22:00 E/W	Byte 225	22:30 N/S	22:30 E/W	Byte 230
23:00 N/S	23:00 E/W	Byte 235	23:30 N/S	23:30 E/W	Byte 240

Byte 241	Byte 242	Byte 243	Byte 244	Byte 245	Byte 246	Byte 247	Byte 248	Byte 249	Byte 250
Byte 251	Byte 252	Byte 253	Byte 254	Byte 255	Byte 256				

Figure 5-4. Organization of the non-volatile memory storage.

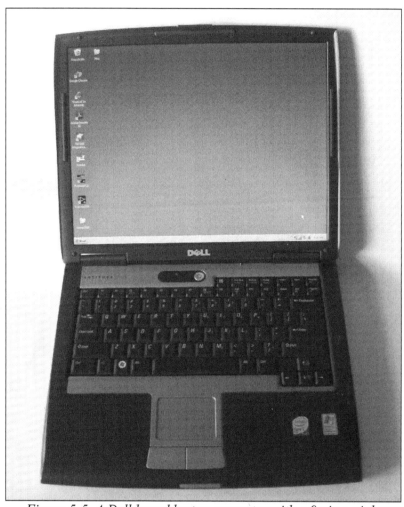

Figure 5-5. A Dell brand laptop computer with a 9 pin serial port.

Figure 5-6. View of a 9 pin serial port on a desktop computer.

Now, we know what you may be thinking: "I already have a computer, and I can simply use a USB to Serial converter." Yes, we know the converter should work in theory. Unfortunately, there is a problem with the practical execution of this approach. The USB converters use internal software coding to emulate the RS-232 serial port. The unfortunate fact is that, although they might work for some applications, we will be using several RS-232 commands which are often not coded correctly in the USB converter. In that case the converter simply doesn't work. Of course, you could purchase and test USB converters until you find one that does the serial port emulation totally correctly... But ask yourself a simple question: Would you rather be doing that, or start building the solar tracker?

Figure 5-7. Many 9 pin serial port connectors are numbered.

Finally, there is one other option you might consider if you have a desktop computer available and would like to use it as the project computer. You can purchase an "adapter card" which installs inside the computer to provide a nine pin serial port. The only challenge to this approach is ascertaining what make and model of computer card to purchase. Generally, many modern computers will accept a PCI or PCI-E card, while older computers may require an ISA card. Any of these cards can be purchased on Ebay for less than $10. Installing an adapter card to provide a nine pin serial card works great for this application. Keep in mind, though, that by using a desktop computer you will not have portability of the test setup for doing your field work.

Software Tools

Here we are going to suggest some computer software applications that are useful for this project. All of these applications are available for the Windows operating system. You may be able to find alternate versions for Linux, Macintosh and other computer operating systems.

The software applications suggested for installation on your project computer are:

1) "Picaxe Programming Editor" from Revolution Education, Ltd., England. This software is needed if you plan to program the Picaxe microcontroller. This software is free.

2) "Termite" an RS-232 Communication Tool from CompuPhase, Netherlands. This software is useful if you plan to establish serial communication with your tracker. This software is free. Note: There are certainly other serial communication programs available that will work, but we have found Termite works very well for this project.

3) "ExpressPCB" from Expresspcb, LLC., USA. This software is used for designing printed circuit boards. This software is only needed if you plan to design your own circuit board. This software is free.

4) "ExpressSCH" from Expresspcb, LLC., U.S.A. This software is used for reading and creating electrical circuit schematics. This software is only needed if you plan to design or edit electrical circuit schematics. This software is free.

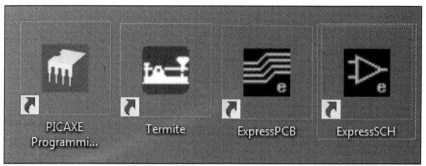

Figure 5-8. The four software applications useful for this project.

Programming Picaxe microcontrollers may seem like a daunting task, but actually it is pretty easy to do using the devices and software provided by Revolution Education, LLC. The microcontroller devices they sell are generically called the "Picaxe" family. The Picaxe devices have built-in capability for serial RS-232 communication. That is one of the reasons why we have emphasized the desirability of setting up a project computer with a native nine pin serial port.

Serial RS-232 communication is an important element of this project. We use serial communication to program the Picaxe microcontroller. We also use serial communication to control the solar tracker when it is operating in manual mode. Operational status reports via serial communication are also available from the solar tracker controller when it is operating in automatic mode.

Project Sidebar: Picaxe Serial Communication

Establishing effective and reliable RS-232 serial communication between your computer and the Picaxe microcontroller is a project priority. We suggest that you make the demonstration of serial port communication a milestone in your project. After this simple project is working, you can confidently move on to more advanced operations with the solar tracker controller and software.

First, a few words about serial communication in general. Serial communication is a method for two devices to communicate with each

98

other using digital signals. This communication protocol has been around for decades, and the history of serial communication goes back to the days of teletypes. Establishing basic serial communication between two devices only requires a three wire connection: That's two signal wires (receive and transmit) and a third wire to establish a common ground.

We are going to establish serial communication between your project computer and the PICAXE-20X2 microcontroller. The setup to operate a Picaxe microcontroller with serial communication is amazingly simple. The circuit diagram is shown in Figure 5-10. We recommend completing this starter project before doing any work with the printed circuit board. This will verify your project computer, serial communication program and Picaxe software programming application are all working correctly.

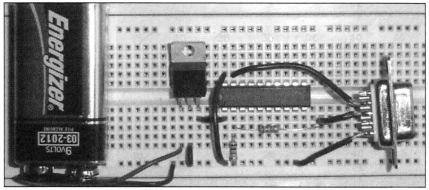

Figure 5-9. Breadboard setup to run a Picaxe serial connection.

The basic setup to operate a Picaxe serial connection is simple and easy to set up, as shown in Figure 5-9. The corresponding circuit diagram is shown in Figure 5-10. The parts list is shown in Figure 5-11. Notice that we have used three short wires to connect with the female serial port connector. If necessary, the short wires shown in the photo can be lengthened to reach your computer.

If you decide to extend the serial connection with a cable, we have a word of caution: Not all serial port extender cables are straight-thru. Some cables have crossed wiring for pin numbers two and three. This is referred to as a "Null Modem" cable. To keep things simple, we suggest you start with the direct wiring as shown. Direct wiring will eliminate the cable variable in your starting setup.

The software code listing for the test program which is loaded into the PICAXE-20X2 is shown in Figure 5-12. The program consists of eight lines of text, and actually only five of those lines are active program code instructions. (The other lines are simply comments.) The five active code lines are:

```
loop1:
sertxd ("hello",13,10)
pause 1000
goto loop1
end
```

The operation of this program is simple: 1) A text string is transmitted using the "sertxd" command, 2) The program waits for one second, and 3) The program loops back to the name marker at the beginning and starts over. This process repeats over and over again. An example of the output from the test program, as viewed by the Termite serial communication program, is shown in Figure 5-13.

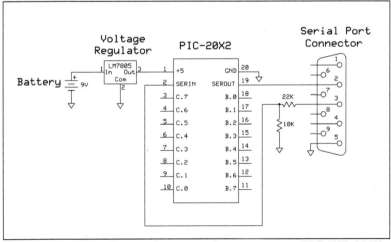

Figure 5-10. Circuit diagram of setup to run a PICAXE-20X2.

Component Name	Qty	Manufacturer / Part Number	Supplier	Supplier Part Number / Notes
Picaxe-20X2 Microcontroller	1	Revolution Education, LLC.	phanderson.com	Must be programmed
Solderless Breadboard	1	Bud Industries / BB-32621	digikey.com	377-2094-ND
Serial Port Connector	1	Norcomp, Inc. / 171-009-203L001	digikey.com	209FE-ND
9V Battery Snap Connector	1	Keystone Electronics / 232	digikey.com	36-232-ND
Resistor, 22K, 1/4W	1	Stackpole Electronics, Inc. / RNMF14FTC22K0	digikey.com	S22KCACT-ND
Resistor, 10K	1	Stackpole Electronics, Inc. / RNMF14FTC10K0	digikey.com	S10KCACT-ND
5V Voltage Regulator	1	Fairchild Semiconductor / LM7805CT	digikey.com	LM7805CT-ND
9V Battery	1	Energizer Battery Company / EN22	digikey.com	N145-ND
Jumper Wire Kit	1	B&K Precision / WK-2	digikey.com	BKWK-2-ND

Figure 5-11 Parts list for building serial port project

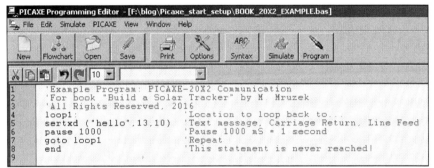

Figure 5-12. Program listing for serial communication testing.

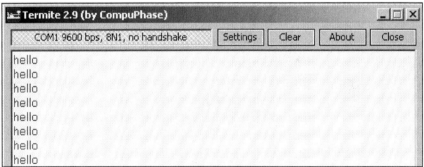

Figure 5-13. Example of the serial test program output.

Begin building this test setup by obtaining the electrical parts and connecting them together, preferably with a solderless breadboard, as shown in Figure 5-9. Next, type the program listing into the computer using the Picaxe Programming Editor software, as shown in Figure 5-12. After typing the program you can check for typing mistakes by clicking on the "Syntax" button in the header. You may also want to save the program at this point by clicking on the "Save" button in the header.

Next, connect your computer to the test setup using the serial port connector. Power is applied to the PICAXE-20X2 by connecting the 9V battery snap. Immediately after applying power to the Picaxe, quickly engage the "Program" option in the software by hitting the "F5" function key. *It is very important to start programming immediately after power is applied to the Picaxe* because the Picaxe "looks" for a new program when power is first applied. You should see a software download progress bar. The Picaxe will be programmed after the progress bar finishes scrolling.

After the microcontroller has been programmed, close the Picaxe Programming Editor and open the Termite serial communication program. (Note: Both programs cannot be open and using the serial port at the same time.) Check to make sure the Termite communication settings match what is shown in Figure 5-13. At this point, you should see the "hello" message scrolling on the screen.

You have just programmed the Picaxe with your own program, and established two way serial communication between the microcontroller and your project computer. The serial communication test program will remain in the Picaxe microcontroller until you download a new program.

Now might be a good time for you to explore writing additional practice code using Picaxe BASIC. For example, by changing the text inside the quotation marks ("hello") you can instruct the program to send a different message. There are numerous other programming examples in the Picaxe manuals. You can view the Picaxe manuals by clicking the "Help" button in the header of the Picaxe Programming Editor.

Serial Communication: Under the Hood

Serial communication is used in this project for two way communication between your project computer and the solar tracker. You might be wondering how the serial communication works. While the specific details of serial communication could easily fill a book, we take a slight detour here to explain at least the basics of what's going on at the hardware level.

102

The serial port communication settings we use are "9600 Baud at N-8-1". The baud rate is related to the speed of the communication. The modifier "N" means no parity, the "8" means eight data bits, and the "1" means one stop bit. Basically this defines a format to be used for the communication, and different devices can (and do) modify these settings for different purposes. If two devices are not using the same speed and settings they can't communicate with each other. In that case, you will usually see some gibberish on the screen. When that happens, experienced operators will start changing the communication settings, in an attempt to get the information to decode and display correctly on the screen.

Let's start with the simplest example. What does the serial transmission of the single letter "M" look like? To start with, we know that an electrical signal is going to be either "ON" or "OFF". In other words binary. We would expect that the M would be sent as a string of "ON" and "OFF" blips. Well, this idea goes all the way back to the days of teletypes. At that time they decided to create a code system in which every letter of the alphabet, every numeric symbol, every punctuation mark and every motion of the teletype carriage was given a number for identification. That coding system is called the "ASCII" code, and the code table is a worldwide standard. As it happens, the ASCII code for the capital letter "M" is 77.

But how do we transmit a number like 77 using "ON" and "OFF" blips? Well, the answer is by converting the decimal number into a binary number. The binary equivalent of the decimal number 77 is the binary number "01001101". Notice that this binary number consists of 8 data bits, having added a leading zero. Okay, so now we know what the digital representation of the letter "M" is, but how do we transmit it?

We could transmit a series of "ON" and "OFF" signals corresponding to the ones and zeroes of the binary number. Actually, that's exactly what is done, but with a twist. Serial communication starts the message by sending the least significant bit first. In other words, the order of the transmitted information is right to left: In our example it's a 1, then a 0, then a 1, etc.

Fine, so we are going to transmit the binary sequence in reverse order. But maybe we should put a signal on the line to signify we are starting to transmit? For that matter, maybe we should put a signal on the line that we are done transmitting the character too, and possibly even transmit another signal that we have finished the transmission completely? Essentially, what we are doing is coming up with a scheme to format the message. As it turns out, it was those format instructions that were established when we specified the protocol as "N-8-1".

Okay then, all that is left to do is decide what signal will be a zero, and what signal will be a one. In serial communication jargon this is the difference between a "mark" and a "space". The standard convention for serial communication is to call the high signal a zero and the low signal a one. Possibly opposite to what you might have expected.

So finally, we can take a look at the recorded output of a serial communication which is sending the letter "M", as shown in Figure 5-14.

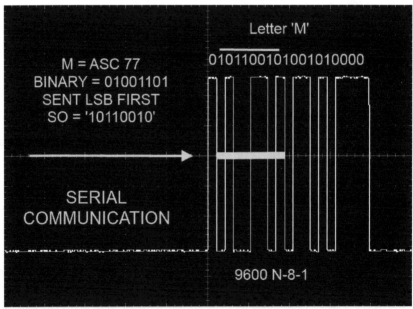

Figure 5-14. Serial transmission of letter "M" at 9600-N-8-1.

We see that the transmission of the letter "M" begins with a bit to indicate the start, and a trail of bits to close out the message. Now let's try something a little bit more complicated and send the longer message "MTM", as shown in Figure 5-15.

We see that the three letters "MTM" are indeed transmitted in sequence. There is a small gap between each of the letters, which incidentally is called the stop bit. We note that each character consists of 8 bits, which comprises a byte. And at the end we see the same 8 bit sequence that was at the end of our single letter "M" transmission. (By the way, that end sequence is "00001010" and when read in reverse, equals decimal "10", which equals "Line Feed (New Line)" in the ASCII table. So it all makes sense!)

Now, we have actually made quite a few arbitrary decisions about our serial communication protocol, including: speed, size of data, start signal, end signal, polarity and how to signal the end-of-message. This actually is not the end of the list, and other serial communication options include error detection and error correction protocols, just to name a few possible differences.

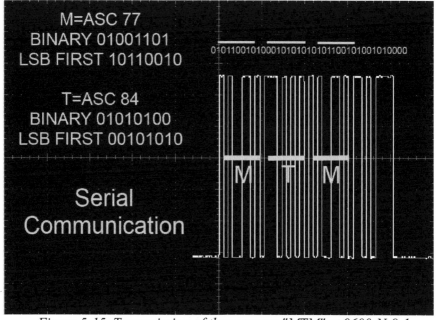

Figure 5-15. Transmission of the message "MTM" at 9600-N-8-1.

Serial communication is used for this project because: The Picaxe microcontroller has the capability built-in, host computers can easily run software to communicate using the method, and most importantly the transmission mode is very robust against electrical noise. In fact, running a serial cable for 100 feet (or more) is usually not a problem, and we did just that for the early development phase of this project. With serial communication and a long cable you can work with your computer anywhere that's convenient, while your solar tracker is busy tracking the Sun outdoors.

Chapter Six: Software Control

In this chapter we explore the world of software control of the Picaxe microcontroller. We anticipate the software will be of great interest to many people working with this project. Even if you don't plan to modify the computer code, it is still helpful to understand the details of how the software works. This chapter focuses on the basic principles of the main software program. This chapter also explains the software's timekeeping method. In the next chapter, we will take a closer look at some of the specifics of how individual subroutines work.

The PICAXE-20X2 microcontroller is a small computer and must be instructed on what to do every step of the way. Those instructions constitute software, and with software we need to be crystal clear regarding the logical sequence of what we are trying to accomplish.

First things first: We want to emphasize that the controller software for this project is provided complete and ready to go. If your interest is only to build a working tracker, then download the program and install it into your assembled controller. Even easier, you can purchase a PICAXE-20X2 with the software already installed from MTM Scientific, Inc. In that case you simply install the programmed IC into your assembled circuit board and get going on the other parts of the project.

We begin our discussion of the software with a flowchart of the solar tracker control program, as shown in Figure 6-1. Computer programs are a structured, logical process for accomplishing a series of tasks. So let's start with the basics: The goal for our software is to find the Sun and track it. You will notice that "Tracking" is step number 9 in the chart at the bottom. Notice the direction of activity in the flowchart. We start at the top and work to the bottom of Figure 6-1. Any item in a rectangular box in Figure 6-1 is a step. Any item in a diamond shaped box in Figure 6-1 is a logical decision point. At a logical decision point the program flow can go one-way-or-the-other, based on the decision. This flowchart shows something computer programmers call a "state machine". The state machine controls the flow of the main program, while subroutines handle specific tasks in support of the main program.

Picaxe BASIC is very similar to other computer languages with the word "BASIC" as part of their names. Picaxe BASIC is a computer language for performing logical comparisons, simple integer math and basic input and output (I/O). Picaxe BASIC is produced and distributed by Revolution Education, Ltd in England. If you are already familiar with some variant of BASIC it will be very easy for you to understand and start programming in Picaxe BASIC.

Picaxe BASIC uses only integer math. This means that numbers can only be represented by whole integers which are equal to or greater than zero. (e.g. 0, 1, 2, 3, 4...) At first this may seem like a major limitation, but actually integer math works quite well for this application.

Software programs usually include "comments" in the code listing to help explain the logical flow. The comments are an aid to the programmer. The Picaxe controller does not read or use the comments. Adding descriptive comments to your computer source code is very important. Detailed comments allow you to return to a coding project and pickup where you left off, which sometimes can be years later. Good comments allow other programmers to understand your code. Comments are also an excellent method to record the change history. In Picaxe BASIC all comments start with a single quotation mark. Watch for them as you examine the code. We try to include comments as often as possible, especially since you will be reading the code for the first time.

Subroutines

Subroutines are code segments which are called by the main program to accomplish specific tasks. In practice, subroutines are called, perform a task, and then return control to the main program. Besides improving the clarity of logical control in a program, subroutines have the additional advantage of reusing code. This avoids listing the same code over-and-over again in the program, thereby saving program memory space. The vast majority of the source code for operating the solar tracker consists of numerous subroutines, each of which has a specific name and purpose.

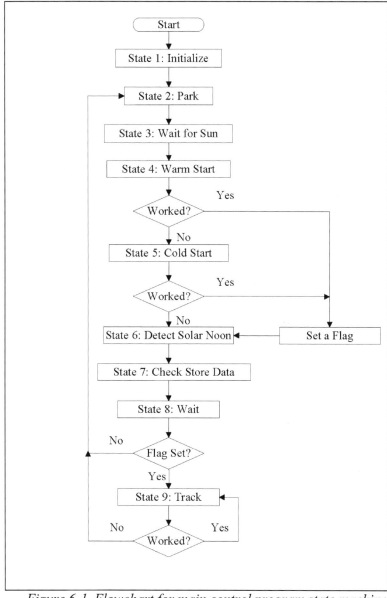

Figure 6-1. Flowchart for main control program state machine.

There are a few best practices which should be used when writing a subroutine. To begin with, it is very helpful to give the subroutine a descriptive name. There is no memory penalty for using long names in the Picaxe BASIC source code listing. Comments and long names don't get loaded into program memory. Only the working commands are loaded into the Picaxe memory.

```
Read_Position:
'This subroutine reads the G sensor for E/W and N/S position
'N/S is input to ADC2 (B.2) & E/W is input to ADC3 (B.3)

Position_NS =  0
Position_EW = 0
ADC_Sum_1 = 0
ADC_Sum_2 = 0

For Index = 1 to ADC_Loops
READADC10 B.2, Position_NS
ADC_Sum_1 = ADC_Sum_1 + Position_NS
READADC10 B.3, Position_EW
ADC_Sum_2 = ADC_Sum_2 + Position_EW
Next

Position_NS = ADC_Sum_1 / ADC_Loops
Position_EW = ADC_Sum_2 / ADC_Loops
Return
```

Figure 6-2. Example of a subroutine to measure angular position.

Another best practice for subroutines is to end the code segment with a return back to the calling code. This establishes each subroutine as merely a specialized service for performing a dedicated function. Subroutines always return control back to the main program when they are finished.

Another good practice is to include descriptive comments at the start of a subroutine to clearly describe exactly what will be done in the code. Likewise, a description of the conditions the subroutine expects to have "setup" prior to being called should be included. For example, sometimes a variable should be initialized before a subroutine is called to perform a calculation using the variable.

An example of a subroutine to measure the North-South and East-West angular position is shown in Figure 6-2. The subroutine begins with a descriptive name, as denoted by the colon. Next, we find several explanatory comments describing the subroutine, as marked by the single quotation mark at the start of each line. Then, we initialize several variables that will be used to dynamically store data while we make multiple readings in a loop, and which will be subsequently averaged. After the data acquisition loop segment we calculate the averages for both the North-South and East-West angular positions. Finally, we return control back to the calling code, because the subroutine has done its job and it's time to return control back to the main program.

Main Program

The purpose of the main program is to control the operation of the solar tracker using a simple logical path which is easy to understand and follow. The main program is called a "state machine". That means it goes from one definite step to the next. You can consider the main program as the "big picture" control system which directs all the other program parts to perform as you wish.

Here, we provide a description of the main program's software control path, as outlined in the flowchart of Figure 6-1.

"**Start**" is the first item in the flowchart. The program starts when power is applied to the PICAXE-20X2. There is no "ON-OFF" switch to start the solar tracker controller. The program starts when power is applied, and the program stops when power is removed.

The next flowchart step is "**State 1:Initialize**". The purpose of the initialize step is to define all of the variables we will be using in the

111

program. In some cases this step also assigns working values to some of the variables. The initialize step also sets up input and output pin parameters on the PICAXE-20X2 microcontroller.

The next flowchart step is "**State 2: Park**". The purpose of this step is to move the solar tracker to the parked position. We have defined the parked position as facing due South with a 45 degree tilt from horizontal.

The next flowchart step is "**State 3: Wait for Sun**". In this step the solar tracker reads the Sun level using the LED sensor and waits for a minimum amount of sunlight before attempting to find and track the Sun. There is only one exception to waiting, and that is when the solar tracker is first energized. (We assume that if the solar tracker has been energized the user has an interest in seeing the tracker perform a search immediately, so only in that special case the waiting is always skipped.)

The next step in the flowchart is "**State 4: Warm Start**". In this step, the solar tracker attempts to use data stored in non-volatile memory as a shortcut to finding the Sun's position. For this step to work, the tracker must know the correct solar time, and non-zero data must exist in the data storage area. If both conditions are met, the tracker moves to the position using that data.

The next flowchart step is a logical decision branch titled "**Worked?**". If the Sun has been successfully found using the warm start routine, a flag is set and the flow jumps directly to State 6, to test for solar noon. However, if the Sun has not been found, the flag is not set and the flow progresses to the next step.

The step "**State 5: Cold Start**" is the most basic of all the Sun searching routines. This routine is designed to find the Sun without the benefit of any shortcuts using stored data. This is the routine that will most often be executed when the tracker is initially set up and operated. The "Cold Start" routine searches for the Sun two different ways. The first way is by using an approach we call "Slope Driven". The second way is by using an approach we call "Full Sky". We will describe these searching strategies in more detail in the next chapter.

The next flowchart step is another logical decision tree titled "**Worked?**". If the Sun has been found successfully using the cold start routine, a flag is set and the flow jumps to State 6 to test for solar noon. If the Sun has not been found, the flag is not set, and the flow jumps to State 6 to test for solar noon.

The next step in the flowchart is "**State 6: Detect Solar Noon**". The purpose of this step is to check if the parameters are present to declare the time is now solar noon. (In which case the clock can be set or reset.) Solar noon exists when the East-West tilt angle is within a few ADC counts of being perfectly level.

The next flowchart step is "**State 7: Check Store Data**". This step determines if Sun position and time information has been acquired since the last check. Then, if the requirements for data quality are met, the data is stored in the non-volatile Picaxe memory.

The next flowchart step is "**State 8: Wait**". This step executes a timed wait of six minutes. (30 minutes if the option 4 jumper is installed.) The waiting step is the self-timing regulated clock that keeps solar time. Considered from a macro viewpoint, the solar tracker software actually spends most of its time right here... waiting and keeping time.

The next flowchart step is another logical decision tree titled "**Flag Set?**". If neither the cold start or warm start process has set the flag, the program returns to the parked position. However, if the flag is set, we know the Sun position has been found and so we proceed to tracking the Sun.

The flowchart step that is executed when the flag is set is "**State 9: Track**". In this step, the software moves the tracker a small amount every six minute time increment to follow the Sun. The tracking routine continues as long as the Sun remains in sight, as determined by the Sun sensor. The tracking stops if the Sun does not remain in sight, in which case the tracker moves back to the parked position. From there the process starts all over again.

Having examined the state machine this way, we can now understand the process from a high level point of view. In other words, we get the "big picture" of how the solar tracker software is working.

Serial Input/Output

The serial input and output communication process is important for several aspects of this project. We use serial communication for programming the Picaxe microcontroller, for controlling the tracker in manual mode, and for monitoring the tracker status reports while it is operating in automatic mode.

The computer software program we prefer to use for serial communication in this project is called "Termite". This program is available from Compuphase in the Netherlands. The program is free and easy-to-use. Simply download and install the application on your project computer to start using it.

Establishing serial communication with the PICAXE-20X2 requires using several specific serial port settings, as shown in Figure 6-3. The most important settings are the Baud Rate (9600), Data Bits (8), and Stop Bits (1). In serial port jargon this protocol is sometimes abbreviated as "9600-N-8-1". These settings are compatible with the settings used in the source code for the solar tracker, and they are also the default settings for the PICAXE-20X2 microcontroller. Note that the communication port selection (COM1) may vary based on the specifics of the project computer you are using to communicate.

The Termite communication window is where you will spend most of your time working with the tracker. When the solar tracker is first energized a welcome message is transmitted by serial data stream, as seen in Figure 6-4. The welcome message provides an opportunity to engage manual control of the solar tracker. This window of opportunity only lasts for 15 seconds. Manual solar tracker control is established at startup by typing a capital "M" in the communication dialog box (at the bottom of the Termite window) and then hitting the return key.

Approximately 15 seconds after startup, the solar tracker will jump directly into automatic mode. In automatic mode the only way to return to manual mode is by removing the controller's 12VDC power supply to initiate a hard reset.

The welcome screen of the program includes a date. This is the revision date of the software. The date is useful to track the revision version of the software. If you decide to change the software source code make sure to change this revision date, so you can easily track which software version is loaded in the Picaxe.

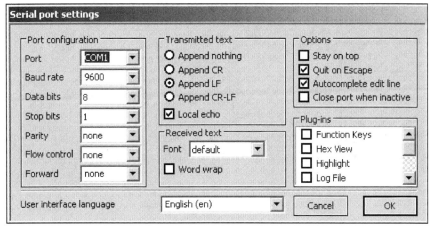

Figure 6-3. Serial communication settings in Termite program.

Timekeeping

The Picaxe chip has the ability to measure elapsed time, but it does not have a Real Time Clock (RTC) for maintaining the global date and time. This leads to a broader question of how we will reckon time in the solar tracker software. The first thought might be to include a standard real time clock module for measuring time. Such clocks are readily available as compact modules. The clock modules also have battery backup for maintaining the correct time, even when the microcontroller is not energized.

We don't include a real time clock (RTC) module in this design for several reasons. 1) A clock module will only "know" the time if we set it first. This forces the user to navigate a setup menu and user interface to correctly communicate the local time. 2) Since the local time can change, we need to consider the effect of differing time zones, and changes back-

and-forth to daylight savings time, etc. 3) Another pitfall is the dependence on a battery for operating the clock. This effectively means that the user must monitor the battery, and change the battery at regular maintenance intervals. 4) We don't know the accuracy of the RTC clock over long periods of time, and whether the device requires adjustment to compensate for long term drift.

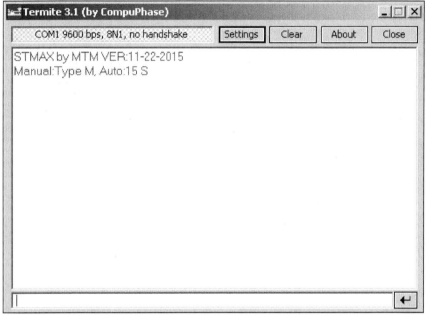

Figure 6-4. Welcome screen viewed using Termite serial program.

Now, we've mentioned that the Picaxe is able to measure elapsed time, even though it does not keep track of global clock time. Imagine that the solar tracker has found the Sun's position using some sky search method. With fairly good certainty, we know that the Sun will be at almost exactly the same position again in about 24 hours. Since the Picaxe is able to measure elapsed time, what if we recorded the Sun's position using the tilt-tilt angle sensor, and set the timer on the Picaxe to measure out a period of 24 hours? After the elapsed time period we could simply move the tilt-tilt platform back to the previously recorded position and the Sun aim would be nearly correct. What's more, this method would work even if the Sun was obscured by clouds.

Solar Noon Timekeeping

We know that the Picaxe can measure elapsed time, but it would still be helpful to have some sort of "universal" time marker from which to reckon our timekeeping. That actually turns out to be fairly simple to define, and also easy to determine when the tracker is operating.

Think about the path of the Sun in the sky... We know the Sun rises in the East and sets in the West. We also know that at midday the Sun will be halfway between sunrise and sunset. At midday the Sun will be at the highest point in the sky. We also know that a solar tracker using the tilt-tilt mechanism will be exactly level along the East-West tilt direction at solar noon, provided the North-South axis has been correctly aligned during setup. In that case, we can use our angle sensor to measure when the East-West axis is (nearly exactly) level, and call that unique and special time of day our "solar noon".

What's unique about this approach is that we don't need to determine solar noon with respect to any type of standard clock time. We are, in effect, establishing a local timeframe for our solar tracker that only depends on measuring when the Sun is midway across the sky. The solar noon detection is strictly device dependent, but that's okay because only our solar tracker will be using the solar noon detection to set the local time base reference.

The bottom line is that we can have a clock on the Picaxe that is measuring time according to elapsed time, which is also being "reset" to the correct time instance of solar noon during a normal tracking day. Therefore, we now have a simple onboard clock that measures solar time and also sets itself. A great advantage of the clock setting itself is that the long term accuracy and stability of the time base is no longer much of an issue. A similar example of timekeeping might be resetting your watch to the correct time everyday at noon.

117

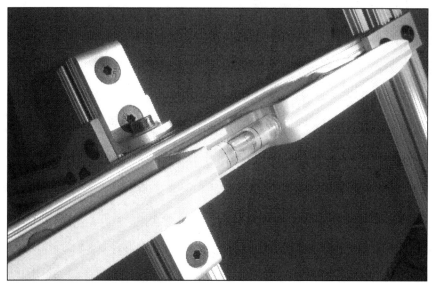

Figure 6-5. The East-West tilt axis is level at solar noon.

Interval Timekeeping

Having explained that we are not using a real time clock, but instead we will be using elapsed time intervals to reckon time, we must devise a system for exactly how we will mark time. This may seem a little bit confusing at first, but the final solution turns out to be surprisingly simple.

There are multiple aspects to the question of how to structure a timekeeping system using intervals. We want the timekeeping to be integer friendly and compatible with normal minutes, hours and days. We also want to store the position of the Sun using the tilt sensor data with the time marker we establish. We want to detect solar noon and use that information to adjust the clock daily, if possible. We also want a meaningful and useful time interval for pacing how often we move the tracker to follow the Sun.

So here is the solution: We have defined a unit of time called a "solex". A solex is a time interval of exactly six minutes. That means there are 10 solexes in an hour and 240 solexes in a day. We decided to start our day at midnight with the solex count equal to zero. We end the day 24 hours later, when the solex count hits 240. At that time, the solex count returns to zero. As a result, the solex count for solar noon is 120. As you can see, this is very similar to time reckoning in a 24 hour format, but simply removes the trailing zero (i.e. noon = 12:00 = 120 solexes). The result is a timekeeping system that meets our requirements, and which is fairly easy to remember because it's intuitive.

There is only one more consideration regarding timekeeping with intervals. The solar tracker spends almost all day waiting to make its next move. While it is waiting, we do the interval timekeeping. But what about the time the tracker actually spends moving? It's during those brief time periods that timekeeping is not being done. As a result, we need to make a small correction to the time intervals to account for the time lost while doing movements. You will see a correction in the subroutine "Wait_6_Min" for just this purpose. The correction was determined experimentally by operating the tracker for several days and calculating the clock offset due to the average time the tracker spent in motion.

Tracking Data

Shown in Figure 6-6 is an excerpt of actual data taken from the angle tilt-tilt sensors while the solar tracker is following the Sun. Recall that the time is measured in 6 minute increments, called solexes. Solar noon is time 120. The units of measurement for both the tilt-tilt angles are in direct ADC counts, as measured by the Picaxe microcontroller. This particular data set was taken at 42 degrees North latitude in Summer.

An interesting pattern emerges when the Sun position data is graphed and analyzed, as shown in Figure 6-7. We see that the East-West (E-W) coordinate has a steady progression from sunrise to sunset during the day. However, even more interesting is the shape of the line when the data is carefully plotted on a graph. We find the East-West Sun position data during a typical day is strongly linear.

The linearity of the East-West tracking rate actually makes sense if we recall that the apparent position of the Sun rotates one complete revolution per day. One revolution per day equals 360 degrees per day.

119

The linear trend line seen in Figure 6-7 suggests that we can track the Sun in this example (to a very close approximation) by simply advancing the solar tracker position at the same East-West rate.

The slope of the plotted East-West tilt axis data is the angular tracking rate we want to implement. In this example, we see that the East-West tilt is advancing at approximately 3.3 ADC counts per time increment, per the trend line equation. (Remember that our increment of time is every six minutes, a unit of measure we have defined as a "solex".)

Time	N/S	E/W
80	412	223
85	414	222
90	420	256
95	430	250
100	427	272
105	413	290
110	435	318
115	425	329
120	424	338
125	424	373
130	421	376
135	413	403
140	406	410
145	411	422

Figure 6-6. Actual data taken while tracking (Noon = 120)

The North-South tracking data does not show the same linear trend line progression. Instead, the North-South data is dithering around a nearly constant value for most of the day. This result is ideal for our purposes, because the implication is that the North-South axis doesn't require simultaneous adjustment for this tracking method to work.

Since we have determined the East-West advancement rate necessary for following the Sun, we can implement this tracking rate whenever the Sun is found. We then have a good probability of continuing to track the Sun, without the requirement to make other adjustments, or to perform additional sky searching.

The linear East-West tracking rate can be calculated theoretically from first principles. The apparent East-West motion rate of the Sun is 360 degrees per day. This works out to 1.5 degrees per solex. From there we need only determine how many ADC counts equal 1.5 degrees. Unfortunately, the ADC count rate is somewhat dependent on the North-South position. (See Figure 4-15.) We have found that 3.3 ADC counts per solex is a reasonable average number for general purpose operations.

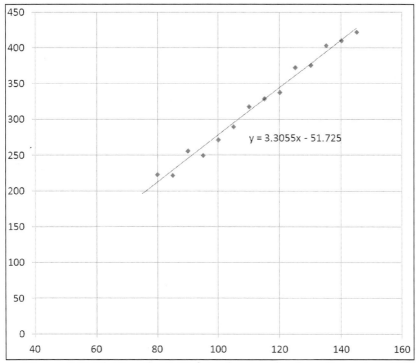

Figure 6-7. Plotting the E-W data shows a day-long linear trend line.

121

You might be wondering how we can implement this incremental tracking method in software. One approach is simply increment the East-West position by 3.3 ADC units every six minutes. We found that there were two problems with this simple approach. Both of these problems were solved with careful software programming, as can be seen in the source code for the subroutine "Inc_EW" in the appendix.

The first issue is, since we are limited to integer math, we must select the "closest" integer for the incremental move, which in this case is three. That means every move would be slightly undersized, since the targeted move amount is 3.3 ADC units. A small amount of misalignment can add up when numerous small adjustments are being made. We work around the integer math limitation with a periodic step size adjustment, which can be found by examining the subroutine details in the source code.

The second issue with execution is more subtle. Our tracker is pretty good at making small moves, but the slight amount of error present in position measurements will accumulate if we always take the starting position as the point to move "from". We would be much better off defining a home base position at the start of a tracking series, and doing the addition with respect to home base as the tracks are progressing. Actually, that is exactly what we do in the software, which you will see if you examine the math coding method in the subroutine.

Software Manual Mode

The solar tracker software includes a special mode of operation for doing research and development. The special mode is called "Manual Mode". When the Picaxe microcontroller first boots, the welcome screen message sent by the controller allows the option of switching into the special mode by typing and sending the letter "M". Doing so will boot the software into the special mode of operation, where 23 specific commands can be sent by using a letter or number. Note though, that approximately 15 seconds after the initial boot, the manual mode option will disappear and the tracker will proceed to fully automatic operation.

122

The manual mode menu is shown in Figure 6-8. The manual mode basically offers two types of actions: Jump to any state in the state machine, or execute one of several subroutines for reporting information or moving the tracker. For example, by sending the number "2" the software will jump to the "Park" segment of the state machine. In that state, the solar tracker moves to the parked position. After executing any state machine segment, the program control returns directly to the user command console. From there, you can execute another command, or exit manual mode and proceed to automatic mode by typing "Q".

It is important to keep in mind that executing any of the numbered states is limited only to the actions of that state. After the state action is performed, software control always returns to the console.

In a similar way, the reporting of individual data readings is accomplished by typing any of the individual letters listed. For example, type "L" to read and report the Sun level.

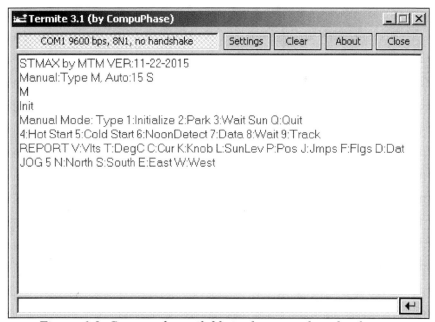

Figure 6-8. Commands available in the manual mode of operation.

The tracker can also be moved while in manual mode. Moving the tracker is accomplished by typing the first letter of any principal compass direction. For example, typing "N" will move (or jog) the tracker five ADC units to the North.

The manual mode of operation can be exited at anytime by typing "Q" for quit. Exiting manual mode will put the tracker into automatic operation. At that point, the only way to return to manual mode is to reboot the Picaxe controller by removing and restoring the 12VDC power. (Note: Power must be removed for a minimum of 10 seconds to trigger a reset.)

The manual mode of operation will be most useful when you begin field testing with your tracker. Manual mode is also useful if you decide to start making changes in the software. With manual mode, you can test the new changes as they are implemented.

Type	Command Name	Description of Command
1	Initialize	Initialize data and variables (Note: Executed when auto mode starts)
2	Park	Park the tracker aimed E/W level and N/S at a 45 degree angle.
3	Wait Sun	Wait for the Sun light level to reach the minimum level for tracking.
Q	Quit	Quit manual mode and start automatic mode.
4	Hot Start	Attempt to find Sun by leveraging stored time & position data.
5	Cold Start	Attempt to find Sun using a series of blind search patterns.
6	Noon Detect	Determine if Solar Noon is present based on defined conditions.
7	Data	Check if time & position data meet criterion for non-volatile storage.
8	Wait	Wait 6 minutes. (Waits 30 minutes if option jumper 4 has jumper.)
9	Track	Move tracker from present position to new positon 6 minutes later.
V	Volts	Report the power supply voltage.
T	Degrees C	Report the temperature of the sensor.
C	Current	Report the current draw from the power supply.
K	Knob	Report the ADC setting of the rotary adjustment potentiometer.
L	Sun Level	Report the Sun level from the sensor.
P	Position	Report tracker position (E/W and N/S angles, ADC count units)
J	Jumpers	Report the jumper settings of the option jumpers.
F	Flags	Report the status of the software flags.
D	Data	Print data stored in non-volatile memory to the display screen.
N	Jog North	Move to the North by 5 ADC units.
S	Jog South	Move to the South by 5 ADC units.
E	Jog East	Move to the East by 5 ADC units.
W	Jog West	Move to the West by 5 ADC units.

Figure 6-9. Manual mode command summary.

Chapter Seven: Tracker Operation

This chapter explains how to put your solar tracker into operation. Once you have the solar tracker running, you will start seeing the different Sun search processes firsthand. At that point you may start to wonder how searching is being done. In this chapter, we explain with greater detail the logic of how the software is actually working.

Putting your solar tracker into operation is a relatively simple process, and the only real distinction is whether you are doing a temporary or a permanent setup. During construction and initial field testing your setups will largely be temporary. For example, you may be placing the solar tracker outdoors on a lawn or driveway for some quick tests. Later in the project, you may opt for a more permanent installation.

The solar tracker software expects the North-South axis of the hardware to be approximately aligned with compass directions North and South. This is generally quite easy to do by eye, although a small magnetic compass can be used as an aid for doing the setup, as shown in Figure 7-1. Axis alignment is not required if you are only doing a "quick test". However, careful alignment is important if you plan to run for an extended time period. That's because Sun position data will eventually be collected and saved in non-volatile memory.

Figure 7-1 Align the base using a compass.

The software is written to perform a special routine when power is applied for the first time. In the most usual case we expect that a person applying power to the controller wants to see the tracker immediately start moving and looking for the Sun. Accordingly, that is exactly what the software has been programmed to do. However, after that first search, the tracker will proceed to normal operation, which requires the detection of sunlight above a minimum threshold before Sun searching starts again. (Note: You can always trigger another Sun search by removing 12VDC power, waiting 10 seconds, and reapplying power.)

One pitfall to watch for during initial testing is the possibility of the linear actuator motions being reversed. This is possible based on the native polarity of the actuators you are using. The simplest way to test for polarity is to attach the linear actuators and use the toggle switches to compare the actual direction of motion, versus the labels on the PCB. If the motion directions happen to be opposite the PCB labels, simply reverse the actuator leads going to the screw terminal connectors.

Quick Start Procedure

1) Place the solar tracker on a smooth level surface with the base of the unit facing due South. A compass may help for alignment.
2) Plug the 120VAC power supply cord of the solar tracker power supply into an appropriate electrical outlet.
3) After 15 seconds, an automatic sky search routine will begin moving the solar tracker to find the Sun.
4) If the Sun is found in Step 3, the next aiming update will happen in 6 minutes. If the Sun was not found in Step 3, the tracker will go to the Park position and wait for the Sun.
5) At dusk the solar tracker controller will automatically park the tracker by moving to the home position.
6) The next day the solar tracker will automatically begin tracking the Sun, once the minimum sunlight threshold is detected.

7) Eventually solar noon will be detected. Thereafter, the Sun's position data will be recorded in non-volatile memory.

Serial Output Monitor

The solar tracker controller includes an option to send and receive serial data information. Although serial data monitoring is not required, you may be interested in following the status reports from the solar tracker as it is operating. That's especially true immediately after building the tracker, when you are doing tests, and when you are preparing to use the tracker with a payload.

You can monitor the status of the solar tracker by attaching a serial communication cable to the controller board. There is a screw terminal connector on the PCB for making the connection. The screw terminals are labeled with the numbers "5", "3" and "2". These numbers correspond to the numbers usually printed on RS-232 serial communication connectors. (See Figure 5-7.) Test the serial cable connections with a multimeter if there is any doubt about pin and wire identification.

The serial data output from the solar tracker controller is easily monitored using a serial communication program. The output from the solar controller will be displayed on your terminal screen as the tracker moves through its normal operating sequence.

When power is first applied to the solar tracker, a welcome message will be displayed on the screen. The welcome message also provides an opportunity to enter manual control. After 15 seconds the tracker will continue with automatic mode.

We show a normal starting sequence in Figure 7-2. (We added the line numbers to make the listing easier to read.) In this example listing the tracker was allowed to proceed into the automatic mode. The tracker quickly found the Sun. Here is a listing of the serial port output, with a short explanation added to describe what is happening: (Some additional comments to explain the output follow the listing.)

Serial Stream Content Sent:	Short Explanation:
1 *STMAX by MTM VER:1-16-2016*	This is the welcome screen
2 Manual:Type M, Auto:15 S	Opportunity to enter manual mode
3 Init	Execution of the 'Initialize' subroutine
4 Park	Move to home using 'Park' subroutine
5 Move_NS	Decide whether to move N or S
6 Move_N	Move North to Park
7 Move_EW	Decide whether to move E or W
8 Move_E	Move East to Park
9 Wait_Sun	Routine skips waiting first power-up
10 W_Start	Warm Start attempt: Criterion not met
11 C_Start	Cold Start attempt: Criterion met
12 M_S 1st	Search using Mini Sky with 1st Pass
13 M_Sky	Mini Sky search routine starts
14 Park	Make sure the tracker is parked (It is)
15 MSN	Mini Sky move to the N. Watch slope
16 MSS	Mini Sky move to the S. Watch slope
17 MSE	Mini Sky move to the E. Watch slope
18 MSW	Mini Sky move to the W. Watch slope
19 M_S OK	Mini Sky search routine worked!
20 Det_S_Noon	Test if Solar Noon is present
21 Noon Fail	Solar Noon is not present
22 Pos N/S=511 Pos E/W=327	Position coordinates of tracker
23 Sun Lev(ADC)=242	Sun Level being detected
24 Chk_Str_Dat	Check if data should be stored
25 W_6_Min	Wait for 6 minutes (1 Solex)
26 *STMAX by MTM VER:1-16-2016*	Header: Data Report
27 I(MA)=0	Current draw is 0 MA (Idle)
28 T(C)=21	Temperature of Sensor is 21 Celsius
29 Flags=000001001	Flags (0=False, 1=True) See text.
30 Noon, Stall, Clock Set, Integral, Warm, Cold, Tracking, Manual, Range	
31 Full_Sun=161	Value of the Full_Sun variable
32 J4,J5,J6,J7=1111	Option Jumpers (1=No Jumper)
33 Pos N/S=506 Pos E/W=324	Present position of the tracker
34 Level(ADC)=134	Present setting of the potentiometer
35 Sun Lev(ADC)=243	Present reading of the Sun sensor
36 Time=0	Present time
37 Volts(V)=11	Present supply voltage
38 #MS=1 #FS=0 #T=0	1 MiniSky, 0 Full Sky, 0 Tracks
39 Transmit Data	Transmit data from non-volatile memory
40 Time= 120, NS= 507, EW= 336,	There is a single data point in memory

Figure 7-2. Serial output data from solar tracker finding the Sun.

Here, we make a few more comments about the serial output data, since space is limited for adding descriptive text in Figure 7-2.

Lines 29 and 30 are reporting the status of the nine software flags. The flag logical values are listed in line 29, and the names of the flags are listed in line 30. We see that two flags are "True = 1". The true flags are "Cold Start" and "Range". This means the last attempt at a Cold Start worked okay. The Range variable means the tracker position is within the allowed range of tilt-tilt position space.

Line 38 reports a running total of daily solar tracker actions. The daily totals are reset to zero at solar midnight. In our case, there has been one successful MS (MiniSky) search. Subsequently, we would expect the solar tracker to begin making tracking movements every six minutes. As the tracks are made, they will be totaled and displayed as a running total.

When you are interpreting the serial data stream output, careful examination of the source code (in the appendix) will explain any specific questions you may have. The native command for any serial output line can easily be found by looking for the "Sertxd" command in the source code, or by using the Picaxe Programming Editor application.

Tracking Routines: In Depth

When we examined the main program for software control we explained that the solar tracker searches for the Sun two different ways. We have purposely delayed discussing the full details of the searching routines until now. This is really the heart of the matter for sky searching, and is also a subject which requires some strategic thinking on what is the best approach to accomplish the goal.

Consider the following: 1) We have a payload platform that moves in a tilt-tilt manner, with one tilt being the East-West direction, and the other tilt being the North-South direction. 2) We have an LED sensor that has medium sensitivity to off-axis sunlight, and high sensitivity to on-axis sunlight. 3) We have an onboard angle sensor that is constantly monitoring the tilt-tilt angles of both directions. Question: How do we structure searching to find the Sun quickly and accurately?

This is actually quite an interesting challenge, and a topic which we are going to examine in detail here.

As we previously mentioned, one approach to finding the Sun is by using historical information of when-and-where it was last seen. That is the reason why we are storing the data in non-volatile memory. However, in the most basic case (which we are considering now) we assume that no data is available and that we are starting the search cold... hence the phrase "Cold Start" used in the software.

To explain each of the Sun search methods, we are going to imagine ourselves walking within a fenced search area. Inside the border of the search area there is a high hill. The peak of the hill represents the peak response of the sunlight sensor. The question is: How do we find the top of the hill within the boundary of our search area?

Simple Search

Let's start with what would probably be the worst possible approach to finding the Sun. Since we know the travel limits of the tracker, we could create a software routine that basically moves and looks at every possible location, records the level of sunlight, records the position, and "remembers" where the sunlight was found to be the brightest. This routine would finish by going to the aiming position that had the brightest measured sunlight. Certainly, this method would be thorough, but it would also have the great disadvantage of taking a really, really long time to accomplish! Additionally, we would be moving the solar tracker a large amount of the time, which directly reduces the time available for solar energy collection, and also creates equipment wear and tear.

Returning to the example of trying to find the peak of a hill inside a bounded search area, the approach we just described corresponds to pacing across every square foot of area inside the boundary, trying to find the highest spot.

Slope Driven Search

The slope driven search routine is a much-improved method for locating the Sun. When you think about it, we really only have two choices of which tilt axis to move first: East-West or North-South. Then, after we pick an axis, we only have two choices for motion of the tilt axis: one way or the other. So, by limiting our motion to only one axis at a time, it basically comes down to whether we should first move East or West, or alternately, North or South.

However, recall that we can read the sunlight level in real time. Suppose we pick a direction to move, start moving, and then watch the sunlight level. If the sunlight level continues to increase we just keep going. But if the sunlight level starts decreasing, we stop and reverse direction. We continue in that opposite direction only as long as the sunlight level increases, and then quickly stop when the sunlight level starts to dip again.

Next, we repeat the process for the other tilt axis: Move in a direction, and keep moving while the sunlight signal increases. When the signal decreases, stop and go the other way. Then, quickly stop moving in that other direction when the sunlight begins decreasing again.

In the example we have described, about trying to find the peak height of a hill inside a given boundary, the slope driven method would basically be equivalent to looking at the slope of the ground and heading strictly uphill, only stopping if we detect the slope decreasing, which would mean we have started going downhill.

We recall the first time we programmed this routine into our tracker software. Frankly, we were completely shocked at how well this simple search routine works! Of course, one of the main requirements for this approach to work is a Sun sensor which has a uniform response. The sensor signal must always increase as the Sun is getting closer. That behavior has a specific mathematical name. The sensor output must be "monotonic". Fortunately, the specially modified LED sensor we have devised exhibits the monotonic signal behavior quite nicely and works very well with this method.

Full Sky Search

The slope driven search works quite well, and in the majority of cases it finds the Sun quickly and efficiently. However, there are a few special situations that require something more with regard to sky searching. In our discussion of the slope driven search, we conveniently skipped over one important point: Where do we start searching from, and does it matter with respect to the final results we will achieve?

Let's return to our earlier example of searching for the peak of a hill within a boundary. Suppose that inside the boundary of our search area there are actually two hills with differing heights, as shown in Figure 7-3. This second peak might be something as simple as a bright cloud. In that case, our slope driven search might start near the smaller peak, follow the slope up the smaller hill, and then mistake it for the true peak. In that case, the search routine would stop searching and miss the larger peak. We must intervene to prevent that situation.

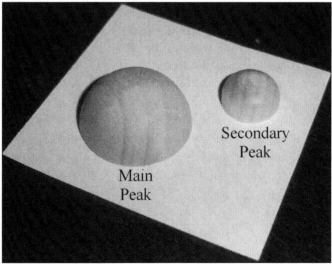

Figure 7-3. Main peak in relation to a secondary peak

At that point how do we know to continue searching, even though we have found a local peak? The solution is to measure the height of the peak and compare the result with a known minimum acceptable height. In other words, we set a minimum Sun level that must be detected before Sun searching is halted. That is the reason we have defined the variable "Full_Sun". If the level is below the threshold, we simply don't stop there. Instead, we continue looking for a peak that meets the minimum required height.

But, if we are at a peak, even though it's small, the simple slope searching is not going to work. So what to do? Well, this is a case were we must expand our search area and look over the full range, moving from boundary to boundary over the full search area.

That is exactly the purpose of a full sky search. The full sky search is designed to canvas the terrain within the boundary of the entire area. The full sky search moves from boundary to boundary for both of the tilt-tilt directions. The idea of this search is to make sure a local peak is not mistaken for the highest true peak.

And so, while a full sky search is in progress, the computer software is recording the sunlight readings and keeping a record of where the Sun measured brightest. After the full search is done, the tracker returns to that brightest location. This type of search takes longer, but is more thorough. When the Sun is found, we can record the time and location, and then in the future it is more likely that we can simply go to the historical location. Recording the Sun's location helps us avoid the requirement of doing lengthy full sky searches in the future.

Defining Full Sun

There is one parameter in the software that is of the utmost importance, because it becomes the logical control point for many different day-to-day tracker operations. That parameter is the variable "Full_Sun". Briefly, this variable is the defining threshold for deciding whether or not the tracker is aimed at the Sun.

Now to some extent, the value of Full_Sun is affected by the characteristics of the LED sensor. However, we have found that different LED sensors all behave fairly uniformly in their response to sunlight. This situation is further improved because we buffer the voltage output of the LED sensor with an amplifier, to avoid changing the output due to other circuit parameters.

However, there are several other variables which can affect the Sun sensor output. For example, in the process of creating the LED sensor, you scuffed the plastic case using an abrasive pad, which creates a somewhat random quality in the final results. Another reason the output may vary is due to the location where the solar tracker is being used, for example at high altitude on a mountain where the sunlight is brighter. Another factor that can change the response is the effect of weathering over time on the optical clarity of the LED. For that matter, even local weather, such as fog or haze can affect the sensor's signal response to full sunlight.

For all of those reasons, we have made the definition of Full_Sun start with a value based on a reasonable average that works in most applications, but have also added some "smarts" to the definition to tweak it slightly up and down, based on the prevailing conditions. The routine to perform the automatic level adjustment is called "Auto_Level".

The approach we took for this routine is to define a basic level of sunlight at 150 ADC counts, but we also allow for the value to increase based on actual measurements during operation, up to a maximum level of 200 ADC counts. The basic level is always reset to 150 ADC counts at night. This is also the basic level that is used when the tracker is first energized.

The level setting for "Full_Sun" is only increased if a higher sunlight level is detected during the course of a day's tracking. Also, the "Full_Sun" level is not increased by the full amount of the increased reading, only a portion of the amount. This amounts to more or less a rolling average, bracketed by a minimum of 150 and a maximum of 200.

This is actually a part of the software that might be an opportunity for other clever programming solutions based on historical averaging.

Stall Detection

Just because the linear trackers are sent a signal to move does not mean the motion will start and continue indefinitely. Recall that the linear actuators have internal limit switches, and they will stop if either limit is reached. When a linear actuator stops at a limit switch, the only direction of motion that is allowed is reversing course, in other words going the other way.

So the question arises, how can we detect that the linear actuator motion has stopped? Well, the first approach might be to measure the tilt axis position, and then check the position again (at a later time) to see if it has changed. This method works, but there are several significant pitfalls in the practical execution:

1) Since the payload platform does not move especially fast, it is necessary to wait long enough between position readings for there to be a significant difference. Said another way: If the readings are taken fast (one quickly after the other) the reported position may be the same, and a false stall will be detected.

2) Another drawback is that the position readings tend to have a small amount of noise in them, for various reasons. These reasons include vibration of the frame, weather and other mechanical disturbances. These random inputs also create the possibility of triggering a false stall detection.

We actually used the position detection method of stall detection for quite a long time during the development phase of this project. We found that the method worked okay... the only drawback being that the time response for detecting a stall was somewhat slow.

We subsequently developed a much-improved method of stall detection that works in a completely different way. We realized that since a stalled linear actuator most likely will be the result of hitting an internal limit switch, at that point the current draw will very nearly be zero. And likewise, if the actuator has hit an obstruction, the current draw would be significantly above normal. Therefore, our improved method of stall detection works by reading the power supply current draw (using the current shunt) and then making a decision based on the result. We have found that this method works quickly, accurately and reliably.

Subroutines: Full List

Here is a full list of all the subroutines used in the software source code, listed in alphabetical order. We also provide a short description of each subroutine after the name. Full details for subroutines are in the source code listing in the appendix.

Asterisk_Line: This subroutine prints the header name and date message.

Auto_Level: This subroutine adjusts the Full_Sun variable setting to accommodate local conditions that may be changing. The allowed range of the Full_Sun variable is 150 to 200 ADC counts.

Check_Store_Data: This subroutine checks to determine if all the necessary conditions have been met to store data in non-volatile memory.

Cold_Start: This subroutine finds the Sun without using any position data from memory. The search is completely based on sunlight detection.

Counter_Reset: This subroutine resets the counter to zero on the watchdog timer. (This is sometimes called "kicking the dog".)

Detect_Solar_Noon: This subroutine determines if all the conditions have been met to declare that solar noon is now being detected.

Find_Integral: This subroutine steps through data indexes looking for the next 30 minute multiple.

Full_Sky_Search: This subroutine moves the tracker to the limits of travel for both tilt-tilt axes looking for, and recording, the location of peak measured sunlight.

Full_Stop: This subroutine stops all motion in all directions.

136

Inc_EW: This subroutine incrementally moves the East-West tilt axis another 3.3 ADC units from the last established home base position.

Initialize: This subroutine initializes the PICAXE-20X2 input and output pins, and also initializes variables used in the program.

Integral_Test: This subroutine tests a data index to determine if it is on a 30 minute boundary.

Jog_East: Moves the East-West tilt axis 5 ADC counts to the East.

Jog_EW: Moves the East-West tilt axis by the number of ADC counts specified by the calling code.

Jog_North: Moves the North-South tilt axis 5 ADC counts to the North.

Jog_NS: Moves the North-South tilt axis by the number of ADC counts specified by the calling code.

Jog_South: Moves the North-South tilt axis 5 ADC counts to the South.

Jog_West: Moves the East-West tilt axis 5 ADC counts to the West.

Keep_Time: This subroutine advances the clock one unit, and rolls over to the next day if needed.

Mini_Sky_Search: This subroutine searches for the Sun. This subroutine makes 2 attempts at slope-driven sky searching.

Mode_Check: This subroutine returns control to the serial port console if manual mode is engaged, after a state or action is performed.

Move_East: This subroutine moves directly to a user specified position, which is to the East from the present position.

Move_East_or_West: This subroutine decides whether the Move_East or the Move_West subroutine should be called to make a move.

Move_North: This subroutine moves directly to a user specified position, which is to the North from the present position.

Move_North_or_South: This subroutine decides whether the Move_North or the Move_South subroutine should be called to make a move.

Move_South: This subroutine moves directly to a user specified position, which is to the South from the present position.

Move_West: This subroutine moves directly to a user specified position, which is to the West from the present position.

Park: This subroutine parks the solar tracker pointing to the South, and at a 45 degree angle to the horizontal.

Peak_Detect: This subroutine compares the last Sun level reading to the recorded peak level and updates the peak number if it is greater.

Range_Check: This subroutine makes sure the present tracker position is within a range considered normal. No motion is allowed if range is not normal.

Read_Current: This subroutine reads the voltage from the current shunt and calculates current draw in units of milliamps.

Read_Data: This subroutine reads position data from the non-volatile memory area based on the data index it is provided.

Read_Level: This subroutine reads the adjustable potentiometer on the PCB. This is an 8 bit reading and is reported as ADC counts.

Read_Position: This subroutine reads the East-West and North-South position from the accelerometer module and reports in ADC counts.

Read_Sun: This subroutine reads the sunlight level from the LED sensor and reports in ADC counts.

Read_Temp: This subroutine reads the temperature from the sensor on the PCB and reports in degrees Celsius with a range of 0 to 127 C.

Read_Voltage: This subroutine reads the power supply input voltage using the voltage divider and reports in units of volts. This is an 8 bit reading.

Report_Current: Sends a serial message reporting current level in units of milliamps.

Report_Data: Calls the transmit data subroutine.

Report_Degrees_C: Sends a serial message reporting the temperature in units of degrees Celsius.

Report_Flags: Sends a serial message reporting the status of all the 1 bit flags used by the controller program.

Report_Full_Sun: Sends a serial message reporting the current value of the Full_Sun variable in units of ADC counts.

Report_Jumpers: Sends a serial message reporting the status of each of the four option jumpers.

Report_Position: Sends a serial message reporting the current position of the East-West and North-South tilt axes in units of ADC counts.

Report_Pot_Level: Sends a serial message reporting the present reading from the potentiometer. This is an 8 bit reading in ADC counts.

Report_Sun_Level: Sends a serial message reporting the present reading of the LED sunlight sensor in units of ADC counts.

Report_Time: Sends a serial message reporting the present time as measured by the solar clock.

Report_Totals: Sends a serial message reporting the number of Full Sky Searches, Mini Sky Searches and Tracks that have been successful today.

Report_Voltage: Sends a serial message reporting the present reading from the voltage supply sensor in units of volts.

Serial_Com: This subroutine is the engine that drives the serial communication interface. This interface is used during manual control mode.

Serial_Report: This subroutine sends a serial message reporting all the parameters which are available for transmission. This is basically a serial output data dump.

Set_Home_Base: This subroutine reads the current tilt-tilt axis positions and establishes the position as the home base for subsequent tracking steps.

Slope_Detect: This subroutine performs dynamic testing of sunlight level while the tracker is moving. The motion stops if the sunlight level decreases.

Stall_Detect: This subroutine determines if the solar tracker may have stalled during movement. Two criteria are checked: The rate of tilt-tilt position change and the power supply current draw.

Store_Data: This subroutine stores data in non-volatile memory using the time as a data index for the storage location.

Track: This subroutine tracks the Sun using incremental movements of the East-West axis, and continues as long as the process is working.

Transmit_Data: This subroutine sends a serial message containing all the non-zero data in the non-volatile memory storage array.

Wait_6_Min: This subroutine goes into a 6 minute wait state.

Wait_30_Min: This subroutine goes into a 30 minute wait state.

Wait_for_Sun: This subroutine checks the Sun level repeatedly, waiting for the level to meet or exceed the minimum threshold to start searching for the Sun.

Warm_Start: This subroutine attempts to find the Sun by using historical data based on the solar time, using data from non-volatile memory.

Chapter Eight: Payloads

It may seem strange that we have delayed a discussion of solar tracker payloads to a later chapter in this book. That's because we have assumed you already have a fairly good idea of the intended payload for your solar tracker.

Some payloads are appropriate for a dual axis solar tracker, while other payloads are definitely not appropriate.

One type of payload that is appropriate for dual axis solar trackers are optically-focused collectors, such as parabolic dishes or lenses. Both of these optical collectors require precise aiming at the Sun. Precise aiming is exactly what our two axis solar tracker is designed to do. An example of this type of payload is shown in Figure 8-1, which is a hot air Stirling engine. The Stirling engine runs on sunlight, as collected and focused by a parabolic reflector. These amazing engines produce mechanical power directly from heat. There are many different styles and types of Stirling engines available, and they are relatively inexpensive because of their popularity with small engine enthusiasts.

Figure 8-1. Solar Stirling engine with parabolic collector dish.

Another payload that works well with a two axis solar tracker is a solar oven. A solar oven is essentially an insulated box with a set of reflectors for concentrating sunlight into a forward-facing clear window. The box interior quickly becomes quite hot, such that it can be used to cook the normal types of food suitable for an oven. An example of a commercially available solar oven is shown in Figure 8-2. There are numerous plans and projects available for building your own solar oven using common everyday materials such as wood, window glass, insulation and aluminum reflectors. This particular solar oven is manufactured by American Educational Products, LLC.

Figure 8-2. Example of a commercially available solar oven.

Another payload that is ideal for a dual axis solar tracker is a Fresnel lens. The Fresnel lens is a special type of optical concentrator, which essentially is a flat sheet of clear plastic with concentric annular grooves.

Each groove is an individual optical facet that bends sunlight to a common optical focus. Because of their construction, these lenses tend to be fairly inexpensive. The effects of the focused sunlight can be quite amazing. Fresnel lenses can be used with such things as thermoelectric generators, or with special solar cells designed for use with concentrated sunlight. Fresnel lenses can also be used for fabrication processes, such as soldering and brazing. Artistic projects are another possibility with Fresnel lenses, such as jewelry making or wood burning. A photo of a Fresnel lens is shown in Figure 8-3. This particular lens was purchased from D&D Surplus.

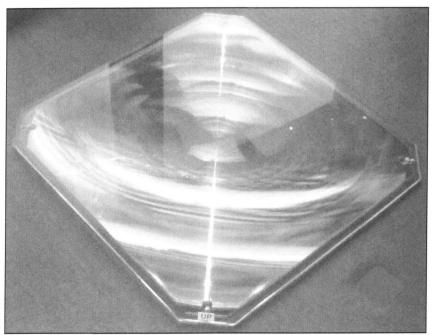

Figure 8-3. Example of a concentrating Fresnel lens.

The curve known as a parabola is ideal for concentrating sunlight, and this special curve deserves closer examination. The unique property of a parabola is the fact it will focus parallel light to a point. This makes the shape ideal for focusing sunlight. The sunlight is focused to a special point that is called the "focal point". The distance to the focal point depends on the exact design of the parabola. You may already be familiar with the parabola shape, since it is often used for satellite television antennas. These antennas focus radio energy to a point, which is where the receiving elements are usually located. We have even seen some experimenters modify existing satellite dish TV antennas to work as parabolic solar reflectors, as shown in Figure 8-4.

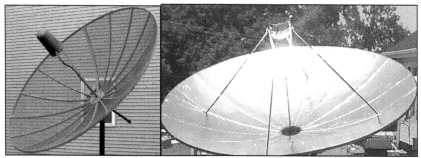

Figure 8-4. Example of parabolic TV dish and reflector covering.

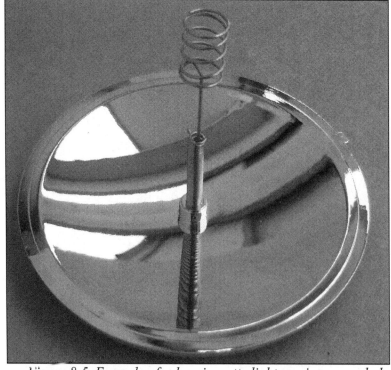

Figure 8-5. Example of solar cigarette lighter using a parabola.

Another interesting class of solar payloads are the "vacuum tube" style of thermal cooking containers. These devices are basically a vacuum insulated glass flask with clear walls, designed such that incoming sunlight is trapped inside by the black walls of the interior cooking chamber, as shown in Figure 8-6. This type of collector could easily be placed at the focus of a reflective collector, such as a parabolic trough. Actually, the example in the photo would be almost a perfect fit for the standard payload platform. Solid food or liquids can be placed inside the container, since the capacity is approximately one gallon. The glass walls facilitate easy cleaning. This particular device was manufactured by Rand Solar, and was purchased on Ebay.

Figure 8-6. Vacuum tube style container for cooking.

Another interesting class of solar tracker payloads are thermoelectric generators. These devices convert heat directly into electricity using the thermoelectric effect. An example of a thermoelectric generator, originally intended for operation with a candle, is shown in Figure 8-7. The thermoelectric element, which generates the electricity, is sandwiched between the upper heat source and the lower heat sink. The candle is the intended source of heat in this example, but the candle could easily be replaced with focused sunlight, such as from a Fresnel lens.

Figure 8-7. Thermoelectric generator converts heat to electricity.

Solar electric panels are another common payload for solar trackers. Precision aiming is generally not required for solar panels, however there are some applications where early morning or late day sunlight collection is especially important. Solar panels have the additional advantage of directly producing DC electrical power. The generated power can be used to operate the tracker. We show an example of a solar panel mounted to a reduced-size payload platform in Figure 8-8.

Figure 8-8. Solar electric panel for generating electricity.

Whichever payload you choose to use with your dual solar axis tracker, the flexibility and adaptability of the 80/20 structural framing system simplifies construction. You will find an almost unimaginable assortment and variety of structural framing options available. We have installed and used 80/20 components outdoors in Michigan weather for several years without adverse corrosion or deterioration.

Chapter Nine: New Directions

Now that you have mastered the basics of a dual axis solar tracker design, we are guessing you are already considering new ideas and directions for additional exploration. Let us help with some ideas for your consideration.

There are numerous areas for investigation and improvement in the operation of the baseline dual axis solar tracker. Here are a few ideas for things to explore:

1) There are various parameters in the source code that are assigned constant values during the "Initialize" routine. It's possible these values could be tweaked to improve the overall performance of the solar tracker.

2) The routine for finding the Sun from a cold start is a combination of slope-driven searching, full-sky searching and optimization jogging. There is nothing especially unique about our choices for doing the searches, and you may have some ideas for improvements, such as the search order, motion ranges and methods of searching.

3) We have not done everything possible with the information provided by the various sensors. For example, the current readings, temperature readings and voltage readings are all available. The information the sensors provide might be used for various other useful purposes. An automatic "low voltage shutdown" is one possibility, and an automatic "high temperature shutdown" is another possible improvement.

4) Build a bigger solar tracker! Actually, that is pretty easy to do, since we have built the tracker in this book using the 1010 extrusion from 80/20. They offer a very similar extrusion called "1515" extrusion, which is 50% larger. They also have other structural elements for building something even larger than that.

5) Connect the solar tracker to a network. Since we have included the basic serial communication capability, an interesting project

would be to design a computer interface on a host computer that is web-enabled, or has other intelligent features.

6) Build a Heliostat. This is certainly in the category of an advanced project, but the basic hardware and sensors are there to make it possible. You have the hardware to move the tracker remotely, and the sensor system in place to know the aiming direction. For example, a host computer could calculate the Heliostat aim required and remotely instruct the tracker to move to those coordinates.

7) Since you can communicate with the solar tracker using serial communication, it is certainly possible to use alternative handheld devices for the interface. For example, it should be possible to use any handheld device that is capable of emulating serial communication, such as a tablet, netbook, or even an LCD serial display.

8) Think "out of the box" with respect to the payloads. There are an abundance of possibilities worth considering, such as thermoelectric generators, solar furnaces, heat engines, cookers, ovens, lenses, optical elements, reflectors, absorption refrigerators, molten heat storage salts, etc.

9) Build an array of trackers. There are many possibilities with this idea. When you think about it, with an array of these trackers you could have one unit as a "master" controller, and "slave" the other trackers to the main controller for working in unison. (i.e. One tracker finds the Sun, and the other trackers are sent to the same aiming coordinates.)

10) Add some additional inputs to the controller. For example, there are two option jumpers on the PCB that are not used by the software. These could be used to adjust operational settings. Another idea would be connecting switches to the option jumpers. For example, you could add a "wind paddle" that trips a switch during high wind conditions to safely park the tracker.

11) The data section of the non-volatile memory is filled by the controller software as the Sun is detected and tracked during

normal operation. The data accumulates over successive days. In principle the data area could be "programmed" at the same time the source code program is downloaded to the IC. You might consider logging the data and saving it in a file for that purpose. In essence, you would be getting a "jump start" on the Sun position learning process.

12) Use the potentiometer to set a working variable related to tracker operation. Our original thought was the potentiometer could be used to set the default "Full_Sun" variable. That would be an easy way to make the Sun detection searching more or less sensitive.

13) The accelerometer module is presently only used for two axis readings, but there is also a third axis available from the device. It is possible to mathematically combine all three readings for improved angular position accuracy. (See the application notes available from the IC manufacturers.) The details get complicated, but the potential is definitely there to make some improvements.

14) We have chosen the PICAXE-20X2 microcontroller for this project, but there are other Picaxe devices available with different capabilities. By starting from this basic framework it would be fairly easy to move up to a different device with increased computational power, or other useful features.

15) Create a stand-alone program on a host computer for monitoring and controlling the solar tracker. An example of a prototype user interface for such a program in shown in Figure 9-1. In this example, you will see we have real-time reporting of aim, solar time, sun level, temperature, voltage and other information.

16) Consider using a different microcontroller which has the ability to do floating point math. In that case, you might decide to include calculations involving the equation of time, astronomical coordinates, global positioning, etc. One possibility is the PIC18F4550 microcontroller from Microchip Technology, Inc in Chandler, Arizona. One very capable version of BASIC for

programming this particular device is the "Proton BASIC Compiler" from Crownhill Associates, Ltd in the United Kingdom.

17) The linear tracking adjustment rate of 3.3 ADC units per solex is an "average" working value. This tracking adjustment rate can also be calculated theoretically. The software could certainly be improved to include a variable tracking rate which is dependent upon the North-South tilt platform position.

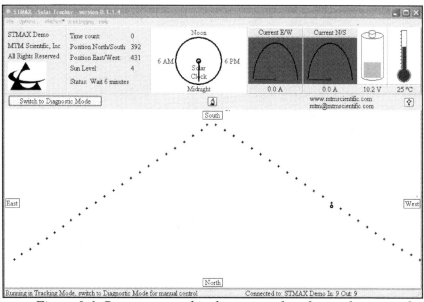

Figure 9-1. Prototype graphical user interface for tracker control.

Our hope is that this solar tracker project will form the basis for additional exploration and development. As you make changes and improvements you may want to share your ideas and progress with other hobbyists. In that case, please consider sharing the information with us, so we can post the details on our website.

Also, we always enjoy seeing photos of your projects. One thing we have learned over the years is that our customers are really smart people! We are constantly amazed at what is achieved and the level of detail, precision and thought our customers put into their projects. We look forward to seeing all the new directions this project will take.

Chapter Ten: Special Information

In this chapter we cover some of the basic concepts related to troubleshooting your solar tracker project. Then we describe a quick and simple way to find the IC datasheets for the electronic components that are used in the controller. We also outline the simple steps required for converting the solar tracker for operation in the Southern Hemisphere. Finally, we provide a list of suppliers to use as a starting point for purchasing the various items needed to complete your solar tracker project.

Troubleshooting

This book would not be complete without saying a few things about troubleshooting. The science of analyzing symptoms and finding failure modes is a special branch of Engineering called "Failure Analysis Engineering".

Briefly, the approach to fixing something that's not working correctly comes down to identifying the symptom, and then exploring the possible failure modes that could be the cause of the symptom. Let's look at a few examples of things to double-check and watch out for:

1) Does anything look or smell wrong on the controller board? That may seem like a silly question, but really, it's amazing the number of things that can be detected simply by looking carefully. The same goes for electrical components damaged by heat. Overheated components often have a characteristic smell which can point you to the problem.

2) Are you sure the controller is receiving power? The green LED on the PCB indicates power status. The green LED will only illuminate when three conditions are true: a) The 12VDC power is available, b) The 5VDC supply circuit is working and, c) The reset circuit is working properly. Use a multimeter to check each of the subsystems if the green LED is not illuminated.

3) Make sure that you have not left either of the toggle switches in an "ON" position. A misplaced toggle switch setting will cause the axis in question to stop working correctly with the controller.

4) Don't forget to use the toggle switches to double-check that you have the polarity of the linear actuators connected correctly.

5) Be careful connecting the wiring to the green screw terminals for the linear actuators, LED sensor and 12VDC power supply. It's possible for the wires to appear as if they are inserted correctly, when in fact they aren't actually making electrical contact. This happens more frequently than you might expect.

6) If necessary, enter the manual mode on the controller and try a few simple motions, and check the data reporting as part of the diagnostics. The manual mode is available for the first 15 seconds after the controller is energized. Enter manual mode by sending the "M" command using the serial communication console.

7) Carefully examine the serial output log from the controller. The output log uses shorthand notations, as has been previously explained. Also, don't hesitate to add additional lines of code to report additional information if you think it may help. Verbose diagnostic output commands can always be removed later (or commented-out) after having served their diagnostic purpose.

IC Datasheets

Several integrated circuits are used in this project. All of these components have detailed datasheets available from the manufacturer. Datasheets are a good place to start if you plan on making changes to any of the circuits. Of course, you can always find datasheets by doing a web search; however web searches can be time consuming because some websites "spoof" the results with annoying advertising and intentional misdirection.

Here's a great tip: One very easy way to get the datasheets, with a minimum of effort, is by going to the website of an electronic component supplier, such as Digi-Key. If you search for the part (by name or number) the search results will include a list of the parts, complete with hot links to the datasheets from the manufacturers, all in easy-to-view PDF format that you can save or print.

Southern Hemisphere

Construction and operation of this solar tracker project in the Southern Hemisphere is almost identical to the Northern Hemisphere. The only differences are with regards to field setup, and the installation of an option jumper on the PCB.

First, users in the Southern Hemisphere should install option jumper #5 on the PCB. Note that this option jumper should only be installed if you are operating the solar tracker in the Southern Hemisphere.

Second, users in the Southern Hemisphere should place the solar tracker in service with the "parked" position of the payload platform facing North, instead of South.

Imagine that you've built the solar tracker exactly according to all the instructions in this book. Now, for Southern Hemisphere operation simply install jumper #5, and pickup and rotate the solar tracker base 180 degrees, so "parked" is now facing North. You will have converted the solar tracker to Southern Hemisphere operation in only a few seconds time.

Of course, by rotating the tracker you have switched all four compass directions with respect to the "South" marking on the PCB. That's okay. The only activity in the solar tracker software which relies on a specific direction is the East-West incremental tracking. (That is when the tracker moves a small amount every six minutes to follow the Sun.) Installing the option jumper tells the software to make that tracking adjustment by moving in the opposite direction. That's all there is to it!

List of Suppliers

We are going to assume you are on a budget and want to build this project with a minimum of expense. Some of the least expensive sources for items can be found by doing online searches at marketplaces such as Ebay and Amazon. Although this is often the best way to get the lowest price, it also can introduce delays in shipping, especially if the parts are coming from faraway geographical locations. Also, substituting parts always leads to the question of whether the parts are truly "equivalent", especially if you start running into problems of some sort.

At the same time, we don't want to list short-lived companies that may exist when we go to press, but soon disappear and become a dead-end source for you. Therefore, we are going to list some well-known companies that can be relied on to source the parts needed for this project, and then allow you to make substitutions as desired, and as the situation warrants.

- McMaster-Carr, Inc. of Chicago, Illinois. This company specializes in mechanical hardware. They also offer some of the more common 80/20 components and fasteners. Visit them online at http://www.mcmaster.com
- 80/20, Inc. of Columbia City, Indiana. This company manufactures the structural framing system called "80/20". Their products are generally sold through local distributors, although Ebay has many of them too. Visit them online at https://8020.net
- Digi-Key, Corporation of Thief River Falls, Minnesota. This company specializes in electronic components. They are also a useful resource for IC datasheets. Visit them online at http://www.digikey.com
- Expresspcb, LLC of Portland, Oregon. This company specializes in PCB manufacturing, with a focus on hobbyists. They also offer free software for PCB design and for creating circuit schematics. Visit them online at http://www.expresspcb.com
- Jameco Electronics of Belmont, California. This company specializes in supplying electronic components. They tend to cater to electronic hobbyists. Visit them online at http://www.jameco.com

- Pololu Corporation of Las Vegas, Nevada. This company specializes in mechanical parts for robots, which includes linear actuators and actuator brackets. Visit them online at http://www.pololu.com

- Phanderson.com of Bel Air, Maryland. This company specializes in electronic components and kits, with an emphasis on the Picaxe line of microcontrollers. Visit them online at http://www.phanderson.com

- Harbor Freight Tools of Calabasas, California. This company specializes in inexpensive tools. They offer an inexpensive multimeter, which sometimes is offered free with any purchase. Visit them online at http://www.harborfreight.com

- Mouser Electronics, Inc. of Mansfield, Texas. This company specializes in electronic components. Visit them online at http://www.mouser.com

- CompuPhase (Informatie-Technologisch Bureau CompuPhase) of Bussum, Netherlands. This company offers the free Termite serial communication software. Visit them online at http://www.compuphase.com

- Revolution Education, LLC of England. This company offers the Picaxe Programming Editor Software, and other items related to the Picaxe devices. Visit them online at: http://www.picaxe.com

- MTM Scientific, Inc. of Clinton, Michigan. This company specializes in scientific kits and supplies for technical hobbyists, with a special focus on solar tracker kits and other items related to the project described in this book. Visit them online at http://www.mtmscientific.com

Chapter Eleven: Project Quick Start

Building a dual axis solar tracker is a major project, and it may help to breakdown the project execution into manageable tasks. Here we present a specific plan of action. The following activities are the steps we suggest you take to proceed in an orderly way with the construction of your dual axis solar tracker project.

Build a Tilt-Tilt frame

You need a mechanical frame that is capable of a tilt-tilt motion of East-West and North-South. This can be built using the 80/20 parts, or you can build one out of wood or other materials. If you are trying to keep costs down, you can still build the frame using the 80/20 parts, but start by only purchasing the bare essential hinges and frame parts. We dubbed this approach "barebones", and further details are listed in Figures 2-17 and 2-18.

Purchase Two Linear Actuators

Almost any style or type of 12VDC linear actuator can be used. Since this really is the heart of your project, it's pretty difficult not to just bite the bullet and purchase a nice pair of these for your project. However, you can save some money by shopping around, and by making your own clevis bracket ends for attaching the actuators (if necessary).

Test & Adjust Linear Actuator Travel

In this step, you want to make sure the limits of travel of the actuators can safely be used with your tilt-tilt frame. The motion of the actuators should be adjusted by moving the bracket locations. Adjust the mounting brackets such that the linear actuators stop before they run into something, at either limit of travel. During this phase you can run the actuators to-and-fro using whatever 12VDC battery or power supply you may have available. You don't need a controller for this activity: Simply use the bare wire leads. The actuators are rugged devices, and they aren't easily damaged.

Set Up a Project Computer With Serial Port

This is going to be the main computer you use for the project. We suggest using an older laptop with a built-in 9 pin serial port. You can use an old desktop computer if you prefer. You need to load the following software on the computer: Picaxe Programming Editor, and Termite Serial Port Monitor. The Expresspcb software is also useful if you plan to design your own circuit board or create electrical schematics.

Test Picaxe Two-Way Communication

The purpose of this activity is to try using your computer to establish communication with a Picaxe chip using serial port communication. This only requires a few simple parts, and is shown in Figure 5-9 and Figure 5-10. This project phase confirms that your development tools are all working properly. This step is a valuable milestone to verify, before proceeding to the main solar tracker controller construction.

Obtain All the Electrical Parts for the Circuit

We have provided a detailed parts list in Figure 3-25. Electrical parts can be purchased directly from an electronic parts company, such as Digi-Key. You can save money by finding equivalents parts on Ebay. If you are an advanced hobbyist, you might consider substituting parts. Kits and components are also available from MTM Scientific, Inc.

Build the Electrical Circuit

The circuit board is the way to go for this part of the project. Another workable (but more difficult) option is to assemble the circuit using a prototype board. Another option is to lay out your own printed circuit board design using the electrical schematic we've provided in Figure 3-26.

Program and Test Controller

Now is the time to establish two way serial communication with the Picaxe microcontroller on the printed circuit board. After communication is established, use the serial link to download the operating program. Once this is established, you can test the operation of the board by entering manual mode on the software. The manual mode option is only offered during the first 15 seconds after power is applied to the controller.

Mount Controller to Frame

Your first test combining the controller with the frame can be quite basic. It is not necessary to have an enclosure for this part of the testing, but make sure that no electrical parts on the PCB are "shorting out" by contacting the metal frame. The first test is to make sure the wiring to the actuators is correct by using the toggle switches. From there, you can connect a computer and test the operation using the manual mode and serial communication.

Demonstrate Autonomous Operation

This basically means setting up your solar tracker outside with a view of the Sun and watching the operation to determine if it is working correctly. You will learn a great deal about the behavior of the tracker by simply watching it for a few days. A search is triggered whenever the solar tracker is "plugged in". Be patient. Remember that the solar tracker is "learning" the Sun position over the course of several days.

Ruggedize Solar Tracker

In this step, you add the enclosure and other parts to protect your solar tracker from the weather. The circuit board must be protected from the weather. You can also route the wiring to be neat and tidy, with cables and wiring secured using cable ties, etc.

Add Payload

In this step, you attach your payload to the frame. If you have started with only the "barebones" frame, you may want to upgrade to a full platform at this point, or switch to a custom platform based on your intended payload and design goals

Software Tweaks & Changes

At this point it is almost inevitable that you will have ideas about changing or modifying the software. That's absolutely no problem, and it is actually easy to do by using the serial communication you have incorporated. Always keep plenty of source code backups so you can return to an earlier version if you make a mistake.

If you do improve the code, please send a copy and description of the improvements to us, so we can make it available to the wider solar tracker project development community.

Appendix: Source Code Listing

This appendix contains the complete source code listing of the dual solar tracker control program for the PICAXE-20X2 microcontroller. Note: You can also download a source code listing of this file from:

http://www.mtmscientific.com/stmax.html

```
'Companion program to book "BUILD A SOLAR TRACKER" by M. Mruzek
'All Rights Reserved,2016 by MTM Scientific, Inc. Clinton, MI U.S.A.
'This program controls the STMAX 2-Axis Solar Tracker via a Picaxe-20X2
'Visit WWW.MTMSCIENTIFIC.COM for latest updates and information
'All Symbols associated with Sunlight & Position must be Words (Not Bytes)
'Single BIT variables are used for flags (True or False Variables)
Symbol Solar_Noon = BIT0 'True if Solar Noon is being detected
Symbol Stall = BIT1 'True if motion is Stalled
Symbol Clock_Set = BIT2 'True if Clock has been set
Symbol Integral = BIT3 'True if Clock or Data Index is integral of 30 minutes
Symbol Warm_Start_Flag = BIT4 'True if Warm Start has been accomplished OK
Symbol Cold_Start_Flag = BIT5 'True if Cold Start has been accomplished OK
Symbol Track_Flag = BIT6 'True if Tracking has been accomplished OK
Symbol Manual_Mode = BIT7 'True if Tracker is in Manual Mode
Symbol Boot_Flag = BIT8 'True at boot and set false at 1st detection of sun
Symbol Range_Flag = BIT9 'True if N/S & E/W position readings are within range
Symbol Park_Flag = BIT10 'True if Parked and no movement since the Park
'Note that BITS 11,12,13,14,15 remain available for use
'Option Jumpers use default PIN names for status to save memory/program size
'Note that Word Variables are 16 bits, Byte variables are 8 bits.
Symbol Sun_Sense = W1 'Measures Sun Sense LED and reports in ADC counts
Symbol Position_NS = W2 'Measures accelerometer and reports NS axis in ADC counts
Symbol Position_EW = W3 'Measures accelerometer and reports EW axis in ADC counts
Symbol Current = W4 'Units of MA (1AMP = 1000MA) Note: Motor(s) must be moving
Symbol Position_Track_Home_Base = W5 'Incremental tracking moves WRT home base
Symbol Temperature = B12 'This is for measurements using DS18B20 sensor in Degrees C
Symbol Track_Attempts = B13 'Number of consecutive Tracking attempts
Symbol Position_NS_Target = W7 'Target position for any NS move
Symbol Position_EW_Target = W8 'Target position for any EW move
Symbol Position_NS_Old = W9 'Used for Stall detection (Compare present to past)
Symbol Position_EW_Old = W10 'Used for Stall detection (Compare present to past)
Symbol Position_NS_Max = W11 'Location of Max Sun Sense in NS tilt axis
```

Symbol Position_EW_Max = W12 'Location of Max Sun Sense in EW tilt axis
Symbol Data_Index = B26 'Used for data read/write in nonvolatile memory
Symbol Half_Hour_Index = B27 'Index for 30 Min Wait
Symbol Mini_Sky_Pause = W14 'Time delay to implement at various phases of searches
Symbol Position_NS_Start = W15 'Start Position for Searching on NS tilt axis
Symbol Position_EW_Start = W16 'Start Position for Searching on EW tilt axis
Symbol Sun_Sense_Max = W17 'Value of Max Sun Sense during a search
Symbol Solar_Clock = B36 'Time. Reckoned in 'solexes' (6 minutes), Noon=120
Symbol Voltage = B37   'Power Supply Voltage, Max 255, Units of Volts
Symbol Sun_Sense_Base = W19 'Sun Level baseline comparison when optimizing
Symbol Jog_Increment = B40   'Motion increment for Jogging search, Max 255
Symbol Full_Sky_Increment = B41 'Motion increment for Full Sky search, Max 255
Symbol Original_Increment = B42 'Place for temporary storage of regular Jog increment
Symbol Level = B43 'Used to read the ADC level of the Potentiometer, Max 255
Symbol Inc_Index = B44   'Variable used for sub-integer incremental tracking moves
Symbol Index = B45 'General purpose index for loops, Max 255
Symbol Dusk_Sun = B46 'This sun level must be exceeded to exit waiting for sun
Symbol ADC_Loops = B47 'Used as # Readings for ADC averaging (Unless Specified)
Symbol ADC_Sum_1 = W24 'Used as running total for ADC reading averages
Symbol ADC_Sum_2 = W25 'Used as running total for ADC reading averages
Symbol Stall_Index = B52 'Loop Index when checking for stalled motion
Symbol Command = B53   'Used to store received Command Character (Single Character!)
Symbol Full_Sun = W27 'Threshold for storing data and detecting Solar Noon
'Note: W27 was the last available normal variable memory space!
Symbol Mini_Skys = S_W0 'System Variable Word, Temporary use
Symbol Full_Skys = S_W1 'System Variable Word, Temporary use
Symbol Tracks = S_W2   'System Variable Word, Temporary use
Symbol Move_N = C.0 'Relay control channel
Symbol Move_S = C.1 'Relay control channel
Symbol Move_E = C.2 'Relay control channel
Symbol Move_W = C.3 'Relay control channel
Symbol Watchdog_Reset = B.7 'Counter Reset (Watchdog Timer)
'Note: Jumper pin inputs & default variables names are assigned during Initialize Routine

'***
'This is the main state machine program segment for automatic tracking.
'See book "Build a Solar Tracker" for flowchart and details of routine.
'***

'Provide opportunity for Manual Control of Tracker before Automatic Mode
Call Serial_Com
'Sertxd is used with the serial I/O pin. Fixed at 9600 baud, which is default.
'Note: In Serial_Com mode any of the States below can be individually executed
'A Mode Check is always done immediately after any action. (Allows manual mode.)

State_1:
Call Initialize
Call Mode_Check 'Exits if Manual Mode
State_2:
'Note: If tracker is already close to Park, this motion is skipped.
Call Park
Call Mode_Check 'Exits if Manual Mode
State_3:
Call Wait_for_Sun
'Note: At 1st power sun waiting is skipped (Tracker moves when plugged-in)
Call Mode_Check 'Exits if Manual Mode
State_4:
Call Warm_Start 'At return if Warm_Start_Flag=1 was OK (Sun was found)
Call Mode_Check 'Exits if Manual Mode
If Warm_Start_Flag = 1 then call Set_Home_Base 'Position used for subsequent Tracking
If Warm_Start_Flag = 1 then goto State_6 'Skip Cold Start if OK
State_5:
Call Cold_Start 'If Cold_Start_Flag = 1 was OK (Sun Detected)
If Cold_Start_Flag = 1 then call Set_Home_Base   'Position used for subsequent tracking
Call Mode_Check 'Exits if Manual Mode
State_6:
Call Detect_Solar_Noon
Call Mode_Check 'Exits if Manual Mode
State_7:
Call Check_Store_Data
Call Mode_Check 'Exits if Manual Mode
State_8:
If PINC.4 = 1 then call Wait_6_Min   'No Jumper, High = 1 = Normal
If PINC.4 = 0 then call Wait_30_Min   'With Jumper, Low = 0 = Slow
'Install Option Jumper 4 to make less frequent motion updates....
'Note that above does not affect the Wait for Sun checking rate. (Variable)
'Note that above does not affect the behavior when first energizing tracker.
Call Mode_Check
If Warm_Start_Flag = 0 AND Cold_Start_Flag = 0 then goto State_2
'Above test should be OK while tracking, since Warm/Cold flags will not be changed...
'Note that Tracking does not start unless there has been successful sun detection...
State_9:
Call Track 'If Track_Flag = 1 unit is Tracking sun OK (Sun Detected)
Call Mode_Check 'Note that in Manual Mode Tracking is 1 iteration
'Don't be too quick departing Tracking routine. Sun was recently detected!
'Make several attempts to continue with tracking to avoid Full Sky Searches
If Track_Flag = 0 then
Track_Attempts = Track_Attempts + 1
If Track_Attempts = 3 then

```
Track_Attempts = 0  'Reset for next instance of Tracking loop
Goto State_2 'Exit tracking after 3 attempts.. Go to Cold/Warm Starts
Endif
Goto State_6 'Try to continue Tracking until maximum Track Attempts
Endif

If Track_Flag = 1 then goto State_6 'Continue tracking if OK

Sertxd("END", 13, 10)
End 'This END statement should never be reached in normal operation!


'***********************************************************************
'End of Main State Machine.  Here are subroutines and other support code.
'***********************************************************************


Asterisk_Line:
Sertxd("*STMAX by MTM VER:2-17-2016*",13,10)
'Date is included for software revision control
Return


Auto_Level:
'This routine automatically adjusts the Full_Sun light level variable
'This routine resets to initial conditions when Dusk_Sun is detected.
'Note that initial conditions must agree in 2 places in this code!
'This subroutine is called whenever a light level measurement is made
'Note that Dusk_Sun and Full_Sun are set at power-on by Initialize subroutine
'Dynamically setting sun level goal higher prevents early search terminations
'Resets Full_Sun level to initial condition if Dusk_Sun is detected (Night, etc)
If Sun_Sense <= Dusk_Sun then
Full_Sun = 150
Endif
'Can't do scratchpad math with Sun_Sense (Called by Sun_Sense)
'Note that this routine allows Full_Sun to decrease in 1/3 window
If Sun_Sense > Full_Sun then
Full_Sun = Sun_Sense * 2
Full_Sun = Full_Sun / 3
Endif
'Impose allowable range limits for Full_Sun (150-200)
If Full_Sun < 150 then
Full_Sun = 150
Endif
If Full_Sun > 200 then
Full_Sun = 200
Endif
```

168

```
Return


Check_Store_Data:
Sertxd("Chk_Str_Dat", 13, 10)
'This subroutine determines if all conditions have been met to store data...
'First, check if the Solar Clock has been set since power applied
If Clock_Set = 0 then goto Check_Store_Data_Exit
'Second, check if the time is an increment of 30 minutes (5 multiple)
Data_Index = Solar_Clock 'Integral Test uses Data_Index. Hence assignment...
Call Integral_Test
If Integral = 0 then goto Check_Store_Data_Exit
'Third, check if threshold for full sun has been attained
Call Read_Sun
If Sun_Sense < Full_Sun then goto Check_Store_Data_Exit
'All conditions have been met.  Proceed to store information
Call Store_Data
Return
Check_Store_Data_Exit:
Return


Cold_Start:
Sertxd("C_Start", 13, 10)
'This subroutine starts from scratch. No time and position data to leverage
'Note: Either of these routines must find sun to be successful and set flag
'Cold Start uses 2 methods to find sun: Mini_Sky_Search & Full_Sky_Search
'Mini_Sky is simplistic: 2 passes. Slope driven optimization on both axes
'Full_Sky_Search moves full range on both axes. Records peak and returns to it.
Cold_Start_Flag = 0
Mini_Sky_Pause = 900         'The 1st pass uses a coarse grid method to search
Sertxd("M_S 1st", 13, 10)
Call Mini_Sky_Search         'This is a Slope-Driven search that may or may not work
Call Read_Sun                'Skip 2nd Pass if 1st Pass works OK
If Sun_Sense > Full_Sun then goto Skip_2nd_Pass
Mini_Sky_Pause = 450         'The 2nd pass uses a finer grid method to search
Sertxd("M_S 2nd", 13, 10)
Call Mini_Sky_2nd_Pass       'Note that the 2nd pass does NOT start from Park
Call Read_Sun
'Note: Optionally more Mini_Sky passes could be added to fine-tune aiming
If Sun_Sense < Full_Sun then goto Mini_Sky_Search_Failure
Skip_2nd_Pass:
Cold_Start_Flag = 1 'All conditions OK: Mini Sky Cold Start Search worked!
Mini_Skys = Mini_Skys + 1    'Running Total of Mini Sky Starts
Sertxd("M_S OK", 13, 10)
Return
```

```
Mini_Sky_Search_Failure:
Sertxd("M_S Fail", 13, 10)
Call Full_Sky_Search 'Note: Performs full E/W then full N/S motion pattern...
'After Full_Sky_Search we may do a small dither around position for peaking.
'This Jogging is an aim tweak. Skip Jogging if Full Sky has found Full Sun
Call Read_Sun
If Sun_Sense > Full_Sun then goto Skip_Jogging
Call Jog_EW
Call Jog_NS
Skip_Jogging:
Call Read_Sun
If Sun_Sense < Full_Sun then goto Cold_Start_Exit
Cold_Start_Flag = 1       'All conditions OK: Cold Start worked!
Full_Skys = Full_Skys + 1 'Running Total of Full Sky Starts
Return
Cold_Start_Exit:
Return


Counter_Reset:
'This routine resets the counter on the Watchdog Timer
High Watchdog_Reset
Pause 10 'Pause for 10 Milliseconds
Low Watchdog_Reset
Return


Detect_Solar_Noon:
Sertxd("Det_S_Noon", 13, 10)
'This subroutine determines whether Solar Noon has been detected and sets clock
'It is always possible to detect and set the clock for Solar Noon
'Which means: A Cold Start, A Warm Start, or while Tracking
'Window for Solar Noon is near level for E/W tilt axis on tracker
'Initialize Solar Noon Flag as false.
Solar_Noon = 0
'FIRST check if Sun Level is above threshold for detection
Call Read_Sun
If Sun_Sense < Full_Sun then goto Detect_Solar_Noon_Exit
'SECOND, check if E/W position is near level (Level = 338)
'Note: Limits for detect range are hard-coded here (333 & 343)
'Result is a Solar Noon window of +/- 5 ADC counts for E/W
Call Read_Position
If Position_EW < 333 OR Position_EW > 343 then goto Detect_Solar_Noon_Exit
'THIRD, Solar Noon has been detected, therefore set the clock and flags
Sertxd("Noon OK", 13,10)
Solar_Clock = 120 'Solar Noon is 120
```

```
Solar_Noon = 1 'Solar Noon has been detected
Clock_Set = 1 'Clock has been set since power applied
Return
Detect_Solar_Noon_Exit:
Sertxd("Noon Fail",13,10)
Call Report_Position
Call Report_Sun_Level
Return


Find_Integral:
'This subroutine finds the next Data_Index that is a 30 minute Integral
'This routine should always result in finding an Integral Data Index
For Index= 1 to 4
Call Integral_Test
If Integral = 1 then goto Find_Integral_Exit
Data_Index = Data_Index + 1
If Data_Index >= 240 then goto Zero_Exit
Next Index
Find_Integral_Exit:
Return
Zero_Exit:
Data_Index = 0
Return


Full_Sky_Search:
Sertxd("F_S Search", 13, 10)
'This subroutine does a programmed search over full sky
'This subroutine is simply a Jog with larger increments & starts from Home
'This subroutine always finishes by moving to the peak detected sun position
'Note: We always start a Full Sky Search from the Parked position
Call Park
Original_Increment = Jog_Increment
Jog_Increment = Full_Sky_Increment
'Start with E/W portion of Full Sky Search
'There is more room to move EW. Increase motion for E/W: Hard Coded
Jog_Increment = Jog_Increment + 60
Call Jog_EW
'Proceed with N/S portion of Full Sky Search
'There is less room to move NS. Decrease motion for N/S to Original.
Jog_Increment = Jog_Increment - 60
Call Jog_NS
Full_Sky_Search_Exit:
'Return Jog Increment to original value
Jog_Increment = Original_Increment
```

```
Return

Full_Stop:
'This subroutine stops the Solar Tracker & pauses briefly
Low Move_N
Low Move_S
Low Move_E
Low Move_W
'Provide a short pause for motion to stop as safety precaution
Pause 200              'This is 200 milliseconds
Return


Inc_EW:
Sertxd("Inc_EW", 13, 10)
'This subroutine moves 3.3 ADC units West from the home base position
'This subroutine moves East if the Option Jumper 5 is present on PCB
'Note: The direction of movement depends on the Option Jumper 5 setting
'No Jumper PINC.5=1 (Northern) & With Jumper PINC.5=0 (Southern)
Call Read_Position
Position_NS_Start = Position_NS
Position_EW_Start = Position_EW
If PINC.5 = 1 Then
Position_EW_Target = Position_Track_Home_Base + 3 'Ideally 3.3 / See 'If' below...
End If
If PINC.5 = 0 Then
Position_EW_Target = Position_Track_Home_Base - 3 'Ideally 3.3 / See 'If' below...
End If
Inc_Index = Inc_Index + 1 'Incremental index used for sub-integer moves
If Inc_Index = 3 Then
Inc_Index = 0 'Every 3rd pass, reset the index
If PINC.5 = 1 Then
Position_EW_Target = Position_EW_Target + 1 'This is the 3rd pass tweak
End If
If PINC.5 = 0 Then
Position_EW_Target = Position_EW_Target - 1 'This is the 3rd pass tweak
End If
End If
Call Move_East_or_West
Return

Initialize:
Sertxd("Init", 13, 10)
'Setup Inputs, Outputs and ADC Channels for Picaxe-20X2 microprocessor
'Refer to Revolution Education, LLC data sheets to understand this process.
```

```
Input C.4, C.5, C.6, C.7  'These are Jumper Inputs (4,5,6 & 7 as Variables PINC.4, etc)
'PINC.4: 6 MIN=True=No Jumper=High=1  &  30 MIN=False=With Jumper=Low=0
'PINC.5: Not Used
'PINC.6: Not Used
'PINC.7: Not Used
Output C.0, C.1, C.2, C.3, B.7 'These are the 4 relays and Reset Pin
Let Adcsetup = %0000010001110110 'ADC 1,2,4,5,6,10 - B.0,B.1,B.2,B.3,B.4,B.5
Sun_Sense_Max = 0
Solar_Clock = 0
Clock_Set = 0 'Clock has not been set yet
Jog_Increment = 15 'How many ADC counts to move during a Jog Search
Full_Sky_Increment = 65 'How many ADC counts to move during a Full Sky Search
Full_Sun = 150'Threshold for storing data and detecting Solar Noon
'Note that Full_Sun number 150 is also hard coded in Auto_Level subroutine
Dusk_Sun = 20 'When waiting for sun this level must be exceeded to start
ADC_Loops = 5 'Number of ADC readings to acquire and average for any measurement
ADC_Sum_1 = 0 'Running total during ADC readings
ADC_Sum_2 = 0 'Running total during ADC readings
Stall_Index = 0 'Index for Stall Detection
Inc_Index = 0   'Index used for sub-integer tracking moves
Track_Attempts = 0 'Number of consecutive Tracking attempts
Boot_Flag = 1  'System always starts as freshly booted, False after first sun detect
Range_Flag = 1 'True if N/S and E/W position readings are within range
Park_Flag = 0  'Set to True at first Park, Set False by any N,S,E or W motion
Mini_Skys = 0       'Number of Mini Sky Searches that were OK
Full_Skys = 0       'Number of Full Sky Searches that were OK
Tracks = 0          'Number of Track movements that were OK
Return


Integral_Test:
'This subroutine tests if time is an integral of 30 minutes
'Note that the test is performed on variable Data_Index
Integral = 0
For Index = 0 to 240 Step 5
If Data_Index = Index then goto True
Next
Return
True:
Integral = 1
Return


Jog_East:
'This is used for Manual Mode jogging (Serial Command)
Call Read_Position
```

```
Position_EW_Target = Position_EW - 5
Call Move_East_or_West
Call Mode_Check 'Returns to Command Prompt
Return


Jog_EW:
Sertxd("J_EW", 13, 10)
'This subroutine always jogs from the present position...
'This subroutine always moves to the peak detected sun position
'The Sun level at start position is taken as baseline for improvement
Call Read_Position
Position_NS_Start = Position_NS
Position_EW_Start = Position_EW
'Establish baseline for Sun level we are attempting to increase
Call Read_Sun
Sun_Sense_Base = Sun_Sense
Sun_Sense_Max = Sun_Sense_Base
'Jog to the East first
Position_EW_Target = Position_EW_Start - Jog_Increment
Call Move_East_or_West
'Jog to the West second
Position_EW_Target = Position_EW_Start + Jog_Increment
Call Move_East_or_West
If Sun_Sense_Max > Sun_Sense_Base then goto Move_to_Peak_EW
'Return back to starting position if no improved sun level position found
Position_EW_Target = Position_EW_Start
Call Move_East_or_West
Return
'Move to the new position when an improved sun level position is found
Move_to_Peak_EW:
Position_EW_Target = Position_EW_Max
Call Move_East_or_West
Return


Jog_North:
'This is used for Manual Mode jogging (Serial Command)
Call Read_Position
Position_NS_Target = Position_NS - 5
Call Move_North_or_South
Call Mode_Check 'Returns to Command Prompt
Return


Jog_NS:
Sertxd("J_NS", 13, 10)
```

```
'This subroutine always Jogs from the position it is at now...
'This subroutine always moves to the peak detected sun position
'Sun level at starting position is taken as baseline for improvement
'Limits of Jog can vary based on calling routine via Jog_Increment adjustment
Call Read_Position
Position_NS_Start = Position_NS
Position_EW_Start = Position_EW
'Establish baseline for Sun level attempting to increase
Call Read_Sun
Sun_Sense_Base = Sun_Sense
Sun_Sense_Max = Sun_Sense_Base
'Jog to the North first
Position_NS_Target = Position_NS_Start - Jog_Increment
Call Move_North_or_South
'Jog to the South second
Position_NS_Target = Position_NS_Start + Jog_Increment
Call Move_North_or_South
If Sun_Sense_Max > Sun_Sense_Base then goto Move_to_Peak_NS
'Return back to starting position if no improved sun level position found
Position_NS_Target = Position_NS_Start
Call Move_North_or_South
Return
'Move to the new position when an improved sun level position is found
Move_to_Peak_NS:
Position_NS_Target = Position_NS_Max
Call Move_North_or_South
Return


Jog_South:
'This is used for Manual Mode jogging (Serial Command)
Call Read_Position
Position_NS_Target = Position_NS + 5
Call Move_North_or_South
Call Mode_Check 'Returns to Command Prompt
Return


Jog_West:
'This is used for Manual Mode jogging (Serial Command)
Call Read_Position
Position_EW_Target = Position_EW + 5
Call Move_East_or_West
Call Mode_Check 'Returns to Command Prompt
Return
```

```
Keep_Time:
Sertxd("Keep_Time", 13, 10)
'This subroutine advances clock and rolls over the day if needed
'Midnight is 0, Solar Noon is 120 (Measured in solexes = 6 minute)
'See book for a full discussion of timekeeping and units.
Solar_Clock = Solar_Clock + 1
If Solar_Clock = 240 then goto Rollover
Return
Rollover:
Solar_Clock = 0
'This would be place to insert a variable for counting number of days
Return


Mini_Sky_Search:
Sertxd("M_Sky",13,10)
Call Park
'First pass of Mini_Sky is from the Parked Position
'Start motion and continue motion while sun increases, with a double-back to be sure
'This process is strictly Slope-Driven. Note However: Motion Stalls are detected.
Mini_Sky_2nd_Pass: 'Entry point for the 2nd Pass
'Note: 2nd Pass of Mini_Sky is from the ending location of 1st Pass
'2nd Pass is skipped in calling routine if Sun_Level is greater than Full_Sun
Sertxd("MSN", 13, 10)
Park_Flag = 0        'Motion imminent
High Move_N
Call Slope_Detect
Call Read_Sun
Sertxd("MSS", 13, 10)
Park_Flag = 0        'Motion imminent
High Move_S
Call Slope_Detect
Call Read_Sun
Sertxd("MSE", 13, 10)
Park_Flag = 0        'Motion imminent
High Move_E
Call Slope_Detect
Call Read_Sun
Sertxd("MSW", 13, 10)
Park_Flag = 0        'Motion imminent
High Move_W
Call Slope_Detect
Mini_Sky_Exit:
Return
```

```
Slope_Detect:
'This routine is always entered with tracker motion in progress!
'This routine always exits with the tracker motion fully stopped
'Exit Cases: 1)Motion stalled 2) Full Sun detected 3) Negative Sun step
Stall_Index = 0 'Set Stall Index for counting in Stall_Detect
Call Read_Sun   'Establish sunlight baseline
If Sun_Sense > Full_Sun then goto Trigger_Test
Do
'This offset in Sun_Sense_Base is allowance for noise in Sun_Sense signal
Sun_Sense_Base = Sun_Sense - 1
Pause Mini_Sky_Pause 'Time delay to allow tracker motion & Sun_Sense change
Call Stall_Detect
If Stall = 1 then goto Slope_Detect_Exit 'Exit Case 1
Call Read_Sun
If Sun_Sense > Full_Sun then goto Trigger_Test 'Exit Case 2
Loop While Sun_Sense >= Sun_Sense_Base 'Exit Case 3
Slope_Detect_Exit:
Call Full_Stop 'Stops N,S,E and West (All Cases)
Return
Trigger_Test:
'This routine rapidly tests Sun_Sense Level for improved exit point
'(This routine provides possibility of doing better than Full_Sun level)
Sun_Sense_Base = Sun_Sense
Pause 100 'Use a short time delay for rapid sun reads, trending and exit
Call Read_Sun
If Sun_Sense > Sun_Sense_Base then goto Trigger_Test 'Keep looping only if...
Goto Slope_Detect_Exit

Mode_Check:
'This subroutine exits State Machine when Manual Mode is engaged.
If Manual_Mode = 1 then goto Command_Prompt
Return

Move_East:
Sertxd("Move_E", 13, 10)
'This subroutine moves to East to given position, exits if stalled
'Subroutine is always looking for brighter sunlight
Call Full_Stop
Call Range_Check   'No motion if position is out of normal range
If Range_Flag = 0 then goto End_East
Call Read_Position
Stall_Index = 0
If Position_EW_Target >= Position_EW then goto End_East
'Relay actuation must be for minimum amount of time
```

```
Park_Flag = 0          'Motion imminent
High Move_E
Pause 35               '35 Milliseconds
'Note: Pause also minimizes starting transients in Accelerometer
'Note: This also determines the 'minimum move'.
Do While Position_EW_Target < Position_EW
High Move_E
Call Peak_Detect
Call Stall_Detect
If Stall = 1 then goto End_East
Call Read_Position
Loop
End_East:
Call Full_Stop
Return


Move_East_or_West:
Sertxd("Move_EW", 13, 10)
'This subroutine moves East or West to given target position
'Detection of Solar Noon is always attempted after any E/W move
Call Full_Stop
Call Read_Position
'Here is a logical decision tree to decide which way to move...
If Position_EW_Target > Position_EW then goto Move_West
If Position_EW_Target < Position_EW then goto Move_East
Call Full_Stop
Call Detect_Solar_Noon
Return


Move_North:
Sertxd("Move_N", 13, 10)
'This subroutine moves to North to given position, exits if stalled
'Subroutine is always looking for brighter sunlight
Call Full_Stop
Call Range_Check    'No motion if position is out of normal range
If Range_Flag = 0 then goto End_North
Call Read_Position
Stall_Index = 0
If Position_NS_Target >= Position_NS then goto End_North
'Relay actuation must be for minimum amount of time
Park_Flag = 0          'Motion imminent
High Move_N
Pause 35               '35 Milliseconds
'Note: Pause also minimizes starting transients in Accelerometer
```

178

```
Do While Position_NS_Target < Position_NS
High Move_N
Call Peak_Detect
Call Stall_Detect
If Stall = 1 then goto End_North
Call Read_Position
Loop
End_North:
Call Full_Stop
Return


Move_North_or_South:
Sertxd("Move_NS", 13, 10)
'This subroutine moves North or South to given position
Call Full_Stop
Call Read_Position
If Position_NS_Target > Position_NS then goto Move_South
If Position_NS_Target < Position_NS then goto Move_North
Call Full_Stop
Return


Move_South:
Sertxd("Move S", 13, 10)
'This subroutine moves to South to given position, exits if stalled
'Subroutine is always looking for brighter sunlight
Call Full_Stop
Call Range_Check    'No motion if position is out of normal range
If Range_Flag = 0 then goto End_South
Call Read_Position
Stall_Index = 0
If Position_NS_Target <= Position_NS then goto End_South
'Relay actuation must be for minimum amount of time
Park_Flag = 0        'Motion imminent
High Move_S
Pause 35             '35 Milliseconds
'Note: Pause also minimizes starting transients in Accelerometer
Do While Position_NS_Target > Position_NS
'Sertxd("DoS", 13, 10)
High Move_S
Call Peak_Detect
Call Stall_Detect
If Stall = 1 then goto End_South
Call Read_Position
Loop
```

179

```
End_South:
Call Full_Stop
Return


Move_West:
Sertxd("Move_W", 13, 10)
'This subroutine moves to West to given position, exits if stalled
'Subroutine is always looking for brighter sunlight
Call Full_Stop
Call Range_Check    'No motion if position is out of normal range
If Range_Flag = 0 then goto End_West
Call Read_Position
Stall_Index = 0
If Position_EW_Target <= Position_EW then goto End_West
'Relay actuation must be for minimum amount of time
Park_Flag = 0        'Motion imminent
High Move_W
Pause 35 '35 Milliseconds
'Note: Pause also minimizes starting transients in Accelerometer
'Note: This also determines the 'minimum move'.
Do While Position_EW_Target > Position_EW
High Move_W
Call Peak_Detect
Call Stall_Detect
If Stall = 1 then goto End_West
Call Read_Position
Loop
End_West:
Call Full_Stop
Return


Park:
Sertxd("Park", 13, 10)
'This subroutine Parks tracker at Home Position (E/W at Level & N/S at 45 South)
'Home: N/S at 45 Degrees South and E/W Level (Can be changed as needed!)
'Parking motion is skipped for N/S or E/W within +/- 4 units of target
If Park_Flag = 1 then goto Park_Exit 'Skip Park if previously Parked & no motion since
Position_NS_Target = 435 '~45 Degrees South
Position_EW_Target = 338 'Level
Call Read_Position
If Position_NS > 430 AND Position_NS < 440 then goto Park_NS_Exit
Call Move_North_or_South
Park_NS_Exit:
Call Read_Position
```

```
If Position_EW > 333 AND Position_EW < 343 then goto Park_EW_Exit
Call Move_East_or_West
Park_EW_Exit:
Park_Exit:
Call Full_Stop
Park_Flag = 1 'Set Park Flag (Set back to 0 for any subsequent N,S,E,W motion)
Return


Peak_Detect:
'This subroutine checks for peak Sun_Sense and records position
Call Read_Sun
If Sun_Sense > Sun_Sense_Max then goto Peak_Detected
Return
Peak_Detected:
Call Read_Position
Position_NS_Max = Position_NS
Position_EW_Max = Position_EW
Sun_Sense_Max = Sun_Sense
Return


Range_Check:
'This routine is opportunity to check position parameters are in an acceptable range
'Presently only position is checked: Optional are voltage, temperature, etc.
'This routine checks to make sure N/S and E/W position readings are in normal range
'This routine can be used to prevent motion...after a tip-over, damage, improper setup
'Output of routine is a flag. True = 1 if within range. False = 0 if out of range
'These ranges are hard coded. Can be changed or modified as needed by user
Range_Flag = 1
Call Read_Position
If Position_NS > 550 OR Position_NS < 325 then goto Range_Check_Fail
If Position_EW > 500 OR Position_EW < 175 then goto Range_Check_Fail
Return
Range_Check_Fail:
Range_Flag = 0
Return


Read_Current:
'This subroutine reads the Shunt for Current flow & calculates Current in MA
'Shunt is 0.100 Ohms, so ADC Counts x 49 for results in MA
'Note that results are significantly dependent on whether motion is in progress
Current = 0
ADC_Sum_1 = 0
For Index=1 to ADC_Loops
READADC10 B.4, Current
```

```
ADC_Sum_1=ADC_Sum_1 + Current
Next
Current = ADC_Sum_1 / ADC_Loops
Current = Current * 49
Return


Read_Data:
'This subroutine reads position and time data from nonvolatile memory
'Reading is done using same format as when the data was stored
'User must set Data_Index to Solar_Clock as warranted!
Read Data_Index, Word Position_NS_Target, Word Position_EW_Target
Return


Read_Level:
'This subroutine reads the adjustable potentiometer
'The reading is reported as an ADC count
'Note that Level is an 8 bit variable. READADC is command for 8 bit ADC read
Level = 0
ADC_Sum_1 = 0
For Index = 1 to ADC_Loops
READADC B.0, Level
ADC_Sum_1 = ADC_Sum_1 + Level
Next
Level = ADC_Sum_1 / ADC_Loops
'Level is reported as simple ADC count, Max 255
Return


Read_Position:
'This subroutine reads the G sensor for E/W and N/S position
'N/S is input to ADC2 (B.2) & E/W is input to ADC3 (B.3)
Position_NS = 0
Position_EW = 0
ADC_Sum_1 = 0
ADC_Sum_2 = 0
For Index = 1 to ADC_Loops
READADC10 B.2, Position_NS
ADC_Sum_1 = ADC_Sum_1 + Position_NS
READADC10 B.3, Position_EW
ADC_Sum_2 = ADC_Sum_2 + Position_EW
Next
Position_NS = ADC_Sum_1 / ADC_Loops
Position_EW = ADC_Sum_2 / ADC_Loops
Return
```

```
Read_Sun:
'This subroutine reads the LED sensor for sunlight level
'The LED sensor is input into ADC1 at B.1
Sun_Sense = 0
ADC_Sum_1 = 0
For Index = 1 to ADC_Loops
READADC10 B.1, Sun_Sense
ADC_Sum_1 = ADC_Sum_1 + Sun_Sense
Next
Sun_Sense = ADC_Sum_1 / ADC_Loops
Call Auto_Level       'This subroutine dynamically sets Full_Sun variable
Return


Read_Temp:
'This subroutine reads the Digital IC Sensor DS18B20 for Temperature
'Temperature is measured in Degrees C.  Note input pin is setup for digital
'Range is 0-127 Degrees C (Negative readings are not allowed)
'See Revolution Education, LLC data sheets and manuals for more information
READTEMP B.6, Temperature
If Temperature > 127 then    'Return 0 for negative temperature values
Temperature = 0              'Set equal to zero
Endif
Return


Read_Voltage:
'This subroutine reads the Divider for Voltage level & calculates Voltage in V
'Voltage variable is byte. Max 255. Approximate reading only
'Use increased ADC Loops so integer division is more accurate: SPECIAL
Voltage = 0
ADC_Sum_1 = 0
For Index = 1 to ADC_Loops
READADC B.5, Voltage
ADC_Sum_1 = ADC_Sum_1 + Voltage
Next
Voltage = ADC_Sum_1 / 23 'Avoids double low resolution division
'Note: Voltage Divider 11X, Averaged ADC Counts / 4.6 for Volts
Return


Report_Current:
Call Read_Current
Sertxd("I(MA)=", #Current,32,13,10)
Call Mode_Check
Return
```

```
Report_Data:
Call Transmit_Data
Call Mode_Check
Return

Report_Degrees_C:
Call Read_Temp
Sertxd("T(C)=", #Temperature,32,13,10)
Call Mode_Check
Return

Report_Flags:
Sertxd("Flags=", #BIT0,#BIT1,#BIT2,#BIT3,#BIT4,#BIT5,#BIT6,#BIT7,#BIT9,13,10)
Sertxd("Noon, Stall, Clock Set, Integral, Warm, Cold, Tracking, Manual, Range",13,10)
Call Mode_Check
Return

Report_Full_Sun:
Sertxd("Full_Sun=", #Full_Sun,32,13,10)
Return

Report_Jumpers:
Sertxd("J4,J5,J6,J7=", #PINC.4, #PINC.5, #PINC.6, #PINC.7,32,13,10)
Call Mode_Check 'Returns to Command Prompt
Return

Report_Position:
Call Read_Position
Sertxd("Pos N/S=", #Position_NS, " Pos E/W=", #Position_EW,32,13,10)
Call Mode_Check
Return

Report_Pot_Level:
Call Read_Level
Sertxd("Level(ADC)=", #Level,32,13,10)
Call Mode_Check
Return

Report_Sun_Level:
Call Read_Sun
Sertxd("Sun Lev(ADC)=", #Sun_Sense,32,13,10)
Call Mode_Check
Return
```

```
Report_Time:
Sertxd("Time=",#Solar_Clock,32,13,10)
Return


Report_Totals:
'This routine reports: Mini Sky Starts, Full Sky Starts and Tracks
'The totals are for operations that worked OK when called during day
'Reporting totals is useful to see progress during a day of tracking
Sertxd("#MS=", #Mini_Skys," #FS=", #Full_Skys," #T=", #Tracks,32,13,10)
Return


Report_Voltage:
Call Read_Voltage
Sertxd("Volts(V)=", #Voltage,32,13,10)
Call Mode_Check
Return


Serial_Com:
'This code allows full RS-232 communication (9600, N, 8, 1) with User
'This code allows Manual Control of STMAX .vs. Automatic Control
'Note that this code is NOT a subroutine. (Hard jump for exit)
Call Asterisk_Line
Sertxd("Manual:Type M, Auto:15 S",13,10)
Serrxd[15000, State_1], Command
If Command != "M" then goto Quit_Auto
Manual_Mode = 1 'Tracker is now in Manual Mode. Set Manual Mode Flag
Call Initialize 'Do a standard Initialize when entering Manual Mode
Command_Prompt:
Sertxd("Manual Mode: Type 1:Initialize 2:Park 3:Wait Sun Q:Quit",13,10)
Sertxd("4:Hot Start 5:Cold Start 6:NoonDetect 7:Data 8:Wait 9:Track ",13,10)
Sertxd("REPORT V:Vlts T:DegC C:Cur K:Knob L:SunLev P:Pos J:Jmps F:Flgs D:Dat",13,10)
Sertxd("JOG 5 N:North S:South E:East W:West",13,10)
Serial_Listen:
Serrxd[15000, Time_Out], Command '15 Sec timeout.Resets Counter.Waits for Command
Character
If Command = "1" then goto State_1
If Command = "2" then goto State_2
If Command = "3" then goto State_3
If Command = "4" then goto State_4
If Command = "5" then goto State_5
If Command = "6" then goto State_6
If Command = "7" then goto State_7
If Command = "8" then goto State_8
If Command = "9" then goto State_9
```

```
If Command = "Q" then goto Quit_Auto
'Following Commands are not states, but rather reporting subroutines...
If Command = "V" then goto Report_Voltage
If Command = "T" then goto Report_Degrees_C
If Command = "C" then goto Report_Current
If Command = "K" then goto Report_Pot_Level 'From Potentiometer
If Command = "L" then goto Report_Sun_Level
If Command = "P" then goto Report_Position
If Command = "J" then goto Report_Jumpers
If Command = "F" then goto Report_Flags
If Command = "D" then goto Report_Data
'Following Commands are all compass motions for Jogging 5 ADC units
If Command = "N" then goto Jog_North
If Command = "S" then goto Jog_South
If Command = "E" then goto Jog_East
If Command = "W" then goto Jog_West
'If Command Character is not recognized then send the User Prompt again...
Goto Command_Prompt
Quit_Auto:
Sertxd ("Auto Mode:NO SERIAL COM",13,10)
Manual_Mode = 0
Reconnect      'Reconnect allows remote program downloads
Goto State_1   'Return to Automatic Mode. This is a hard jump.
Time_Out:
Call Counter_Reset  'Resets the counter
Goto Serial_Listen   'Return to listen for Command


Serial_Report:
'This subroutine reports system information via RS-232 serial connection
'Parameters are 9600 Baud, N,8,1 (8 Data Bits, 1 Stop bit, No Parity, No Flow)
'Reporting is generally done at start of any call to a 6 minute wait.
Call Asterisk_Line
Call Report_Current
Call Report_Degrees_C
Call Report_Flags
Call Report_Full_Sun
Call Report_Jumpers
Call Report_Position
Call Report_Pot_Level
Call Report_Sun_Level
Call Report_Time
Call Report_Voltage
Call Report_Totals
Return
```

```
Set_Home_Base:
'This routine reads current position and sets home base for subsequent tracking
Call Read_Position
Position_Track_Home_Base = Position_EW
Return


Stall_Detect:
'Sertxd("Stall_Detect ", 13, 10)
'This subroutine detects if movement is stalled and sets a flag
'This routines uses 2 different criterion: Position and Current Draw (Min & Max)
'Routine initializes on 1st loop and checks for position stall on 20th loop
'As written (1/20 scc with 20 loops) position stall checking is every 1 second
'The 2nd criterion of current/amps detection works well and is fast
'See discussion in book for full explanation of this process.
Stall = 0
'Note that calling routines should always initialize Stall_Index before call
Stall_Index = Stall_Index + 1
If Stall_Index = 1 then goto Baseline     'Note: Add time delay either case
If Stall_Index > 1 then goto Check        'Note: Add time delay either case
Baseline:
        Call Read_Position
        Position_NS_Old = Position_NS
        Position_EW_Old = Position_EW
        Pause 50 'Provides 1/20 second delay for motion to happen
        Return    'Baseline position has been established
Check:
'The check for a current/amperage stall-obstruction is performed every call
Call Read_Current
If Current < 50 then goto Set_Stall       'Limit switch tripped. No current
If Current > 2000 then goto Set_Stall     'Overcurrent: Obstruction, etc.
'Check for motion stall is only performed each 20th call.
Pause 50 'Provides 1/20 second delay for motion to happen
If Stall_Index = 20 then
Stall_Index = 0      'Resets the Stall Index for next set of iterations
Call Read_Position
If Position_NS = Position_NS_Old AND Position_EW = Position_EW_Old then goto Set_Stall
Endif
Return
Set_Stall:
Stall = 1
Sertxd ("STALL",13,10)
Return
```

187

```
Store_Data:
'This subroutine stores position & time data in nonvolatile memory for future reference
'Format: Position N/S, Position E/W while using the Solar Clock as the Index
'Note that 4 bytes are used... spare byte at end of data is for future use (Day, Month, etc.)
'See book for discussion of the data format used for non-volatile string data
Call Read_Position
Write Data_Index,Word Position_NS, Word Position_EW
Return


Track:
Sertxd("Track", 13, 10)
'This subroutine tracks the sun after successful Warm or Cold Start
'Note: Must continue finding sun to be successful and continue setting flag
'Home Base is used for tracking reference
'Home Base reference avoids error accumulation of small incremental movements
'Home Base must be updated whenever aim optimization is done (Jog, CS, WS)
Track_Flag = 0
'First try an incremental move, which theoretically should work OK
'Incremental move also 'centers' position to theoretical for search baseline
Call Inc_EW
Call Read_Sun
If Sun_Sense > Full_Sun then goto Set_Flag
'Simple Incremental did not work...resort to a jogging search pattern (with peaking)
'Note that this will require using a new Home Base for tracking
Call Jog_NS
Call Jog_EW
Call Read_Sun
If Sun_Sense < Full_Sun then goto Track_Exit
Call Set_Home_Base 'Must reset Home Base because of the Jog motion
Set_Flag:
Track_Flag = 1 'All conditions OK: Tracking worked!(Inc or Jog)
Tracks = Tracks + 1          'Running Total of Tracks
Return
Track_Exit:
Return


Transmit_Data:
'This subroutine transmits stored non-volatile data out via the Serial Port
'This subroutine only transmits data which is non-zero
'Note: Data is stored only every 5 solexes (30 minutes)
Sertxd("Transmit Data", 13, 10)
For Index =0 to 239 Step 5
Read Index, Word Position_NS, Word Position_EW
If Position_NS=0 AND Position_EW=0 then goto Do_Not_Print
```

```
Sertxd("Time= ",#Index,44,32,"NS= ",#Position_NS,44,32,"EW=
",#Position_EW,44,32,13,10)
Do_Not_Print:
Next
'Read position now to force variables to have the current E/W & N/S position
Call Read_Position
Return


Wait_6_Min:
Sertxd("W_6_Min", 13, 10)
'This subroutine waits 6 minutes. No exit until then. Advances clock.
'Serial reporting is done here. This limits report frequency to 6 minutes
'This subroutine also resets the Watchdog Timer every minute ('Kicks the Dog')
'Subtracting correction offset of 1260 msec per minute based on tests.
'See book for discussion of incremental timekeeping and the correction offset
Call Serial_Report
Call Transmit_Data
For Index = 1 to 6
Call Counter_Reset 'High on Pin B.7, Symbol Watchdog_Reset
'Per bench testing: Watchdog must be reset every 17.5 minutes, or less
Pause 58740 'Note: Ignores the 10 Milliseconds used for Watchdog Timer Reset
Next Index
'Advance the clock
Call Keep_Time
Return


Wait_30_Min:
Sertxd("W_30_Min", 13, 10)
'This subroutine waits 30 minutes.  No exit unless the data boundary detected
'Purpose of boundary exit is to keep motion interval aligned with data interval
For Half_Hour_Index = 1 to 5
Call Wait_6_Min
'Perform test for 1/2 hour time synchronization with data logging
Data_Index = Solar_Clock      'Integral Test uses Data_Index
Call Integral_Test              'Test to determine time is 30 min integral
If Integral = 1 then goto Exit_Wait_30_Min
Next Half_Hour_Index
Exit_Wait_30_Min:
Return


Wait_for_Sun:
Sertxd("Wait_Sun", 13, 10)
Sun_Wait_Continue:
'This subroutine waits for the sun during the night, cloudy periods, etc.
```

'Special Case: At 1st Powerup Wait_for_Sun is skipped (Tracker moves when plugged-in)
'The dusk sun checks are done every 6 minutes, except for Special Case above.
Call Read_Sun
If Sun_Sense > Dusk_Sun then goto Exit_Wait_for_Sun
If Boot_Flag = 1 then goto Exit_Wait_for_Sun
Call Wait_6_Min   'The Counter Reset for Watchdog Timer is in the 1 minute loop
GoTo Sun_Wait_Continue   'Looping point chosen to skip serial port transmissions
Exit_Wait_for_Sun:
Boot_Flag = 0   'Wait_for_Sun is only skipped at 1st power
Return

Warm_Start:
Sertxd("W_Start", 13, 10)
'This subroutine attempts to use existing time and position data
'Note: Must find sun to be successful and set the flag
Warm_Start_Flag = 0
'FIRST, see if the clock has been set since powerup
If Clock_Set = 0 then goto Warm_Start_Exit
'SECOND, Find Data_Index of closest integral time (30 min)
Data_Index = Solar_Clock
Call Find_Integral
'THIRD, see if there is non-zero data in EEPROM location at the location
'Data_Index is used when reading data, and will be an integral 30 min
Call Read_Data
If Position_NS_Target = 0 then goto Warm_Start_Exit
If Position_EW_Target = 0 then goto Warm_Start_Exit
'FOURTH, move to EEPROM position. N/S then E/W
Call Move_North_or_South
Call Move_East_or_West
Call Read_Sun
If Sun_Sense < Full_Sun then goto Warm_Start_Exit
Warm_Start_Flag = 1 'All conditions OK: Warm Start worked!
Return
Warm_Start_Exit:
Return

Index

1N4002, 45
2N3904, 45
80/20, 20, 158
accelerometer module, 55
adapter card, 96
American Educational Products, 142
analog-to-digital, 65
ASCII, 103
averaging, 66
barebones, 31
brackets, 36
BS250, 41
comments, 108
compass, 125
CompuPhase, 159
D&D Surplus, 143
Dell Latitude, 93
Digi-Key, 61, 156, 158
Diodes, 54
DS18B20., 74
electrolytic capacitor, 53
enclosure, 29
Expresspcb, 158
ExpressPCB, 97
ExpressSCH, 97
feedthrough, 59
Floor Mount Base, 27
Fresnel lens, 142
Full Sky Search, 132
Full Sun, 133
fuse, 38
Harbor Freight Tools, 159

hinges, 24
IC Datasheets, 156
integer math, 86
integrated circuits, 56
Interval Timekeeping, 118
Jameco Electronics, 158
LED, 55, 68
limit switches, 80
linear actuator, 35
LM7805, 39
LT1006, 71
Manual Mode, 122
McMaster-Carr, 158
memory organization, 88
MEMS, 77
Microchip Technology, Inc, 151
MMA7361, 77
Mouser Electronics, 159
MTM Scientific, Inc, 159
multimeter, 57
N-8-1, 104
non-volatile data, 91
Null Modem, 99
option jumpers, 81
parabola, 143
Park position, 78
parts list, 21, 61
payloads, 141
Phanderson.com, 159
PIC18F4550, 151
Picaxe, 98
Picaxe BASIC, 108
Picaxe Programming Editor, 97

PICAXE-20X2, 85
polarity protection, 38
Pololu Corporation, 159
potentiometer, 82
power supply, 37
printed circuit board, 45
program space, 90
Project Computer, 92
Quick Start, 161
Rand Solar, 145
real time clock, 115
relays, 43
resistors, 57
Revolution Education, LLC, 159
ripple binary counter, 41
RS-232 serial communication, 87
scuffing, 69
sensors, 65
serial communication, 98
shunt, 74
silkscreen layer, 50
Simple Search, 130
Slope Driven Search, 131
software applications, 97
solar cell, 67
Solar Noon, 117
solar oven, 142
Soldering, 51

solex, 118
source code, 165
Southern Hemisphere, 157
specifications, 15
Stall Detection, 135
state machine, 108
Stirling engine, 141
Subroutines, 108
Subroutines: Full List, 136
Sun pointer, 28
Sun sensor, 66
Suppliers, 157
System Memory, 92
temperature sensor, 55
Termite, 97
thermoelectric generators, 146
tilt-rotate, 17
tilt-tilt, 15
Timekeeping, 115
toggle switches, 45
transistors, 54
Troubleshooting, 155
USB communication, 87
USB to Serial converter, 96
variable space, 89
variables, 86
voltage divider, 75
voltage regulator, 54
watchdog timer, 40